LOUISIANA STATE UNIVERSITY STUDIES

Biological Science Series

St. John P. Chilton, Editor

———

Number Four

Dynamics of Even-Aged Forest Stands

1961

LOUISIANA STATE UNIVERSITY STUDIES

Richard J. Russell, General Editor

The Louisiana State University Studies Series was established to publish the results of research by faculty members, staff, and graduate students of the University. Manuscripts of exceptional merit from sources other than the aforementioned are considered for publication provided they deal with subjects of particular interest to Louisiana.

The Studies originally appeared as a unified series consisting of forty-two numbers, published between the years 1931 and 1941. In 1951 the Studies were reactivated and are now being issued in the following series: Social Sciences, Humanities, Biological Sciences, and Physical Sciences. Other series may be established as the need arises.

The Studies in each series will be numbered only serially without volume designation.

Requests for exchanges should be addressed to the Gift and Exchange Division, Louisiana State University Library, Baton Rouge. All other communications should be addressed to the Louisiana State University Press, Baton Rouge.

DYNAMICS OF
EVEN-AGED FOREST STANDS

by

M. S. CZARNOWSKI

LOUISIANA STATE UNIVERSITY PRESS

BATON ROUGE

M C M L X I

PREFACE

This publication is an attempt to outline the theory and practice of that branch of forest ecology which may be called the dynamics
of even-aged forest stands. I have tried to express and to explain in a
comprehensive way the phenomena which are the subject of the study. At
the risk of repetition, therefore, I presented my conceptions briefly
and simply in Chapter I, intending to inform the reader of my conclusions before presenting arguments and numerical evidence in support of
these conclusions. I make no claim that all problems concerning the
subject are solved; I intend only to arouse the reader's interest in the
subject which is of considerable importance to future forest research
and practice.

The study presented here was developed during 1959 in the School
of Forestry of the Louisiana State University Agricultural Experiment
Station in Baton Rouge, Louisiana, as a result of an invitation extended
by the University and encouragement given to me by Mr. P. A. Briegleb,
Director of the Southern Forest Experiment Station in New Orleans,
Louisiana. Since southern pine sites have the greatest possibilities of
growth among all pine sites in our hemisphere, forest stands in Louisiana represent a suitable subject for the study of stand dynamics.

My work and presentation of this material became possible thanks
to the interest and help of Dr. Paul Y. Burns, Director of the School of

v

Forestry of Louisiana State University, and I am grateful to the author-
ities of the University for enabling me to prepare this publication.

Thanks are due also to those individuals and organizations which permit-
ted me to use their unpublished experimental data; namely, Mr. W. F.
Mann, Jr., Southern Forest Experiment Station; Mr. Hans Enghardt, Louisiana Forestry Commission; and Professor B. A. Bateman, Louisiana State
University. All analyses, interpretations, and inferences based on
these unpublished data are my own and are not necessarily concurred with
by the Southern Forest Experiment Station, Louisiana Forestry Commission
nor the University.

I would like also to give my sincere thanks to all the persons
who have read one or more chapters of the manuscript and have made cri-
tical remarks; particularly to Dr. Burns, who critically read all the
manuscript and gave his linguistic and terminological help; to Professor
R. W. McDermid, Louisiana State University School of Forestry, who read
nearly all the text; to Professor O. Rojo, National University in
Merida, Venezuela, who reviewed my work from mathematical and methodical
points of view; to Professor W. H. Meyer, Yale School of Forestry, who
reviewed the entire manuscript; and to Mrs. M. Stern and Mrs. A. Seal
for their patience in typing my drafts.

M. S. Czarnowski

TABLE OF CONTENTS

Page

vii

LIST OF FIGURES

ix

LIST OF TABLES

Page

DYNAMICS OF EVEN-AGED

FOREST STANDS

Chapter I

INTRODUCTION

In forestry, an aggregation of trees occupying a specific area and sufficiently uniform in species composition, age arrangement, and condition as to be distinguishable from the forest on adjoining areas is called a forest stand. For the purpose of finding relations between individual trees in the stand and between various stand characteristics, a pure, even-aged stand is best, because it represents the least complicated kind of forest community. Pure, even-aged stands are frequently found in nature, and they are often the kind of stand chosen as a goal of forest management.

Individual pure, even-aged stands differ with regard to number of trees per surface unit and average tree diameter, as well as to age, height, and volume per surface unit. This list includes only five stand parameters; however, stands occur in so many combinations of these characteristics that relationships between them have hitherto not been unraveled satisfactorily by quantitative methods. Long, cumbersome tabulations which describe stands by means of these characteristics have been wittily named, by practising foresters in Europe, "cemeteries of numbers." Table 1 shows a portion of one of these assemblages for Scots pine (_Pinus sylvestris_ L.) stands on different sites in Poland (from Jedliński _et al._, 1932). The stands described in Table 1 are of several

3

TABLE 1. Average heights, diameters, and numbers of trees in selected Scots pine stands of different ages on various sites and at identical degrees of stocking (compactness). (From Jedliński et al., 1932).

Age in years	Av. height in feet	Av. d.b.h. in inches	Number of trees per acre
a	H	d	N
31	36.1	4.3	1475
36	37.1	5.0	978
44	38.7	4.9	956
48	41.0	5.0	923
51	42.3	5.3	815
42	43.3	5.8	790
39	45.5	5.7	876
67	46.8	6.4	561
41	47.8	6.0	789
43	55.7	7.2	632
71	61.6	8.4	374
75	66.5	8.6	402
67	66.5	9.1	372
59	71.7	9.4	319
60	78.7	11.0	298
96	79.0	13.0	170

different ages but are approximately equal in degree of "compactness" or stocking. What this degree is will be explained in one of the following chapters. It is sufficient at this point to state that there are methods of determining this degree.

In Table 1 the relationships between diameter, height, and number of trees are not obvious. These relationships would be even more obscure if the table included stands of different degrees of stocking.

Studies of the growth of pure, even-aged stands have shown that stands grown in the same locality, in identical site conditions, attain the same height at a given age, while number of trees per surface unit and mean stand diameter oscillate within wide limits. As number of trees increases, mean stand diameter decreases, as illustrated by Table 2.

TABLE 2.   Relationship of number of trees to average diameter and average height in pure, even-aged stands (from measurements by the author).

Age in years	Av. height in feet	Av. d.b.h. in inches	Number of trees per acre
a	H	d	N
36	47.6	6.5	613
36	47.2	5.5	718
35	46.6	5.1	830
37	46.6	4.9	1185

The research of G. Baader (1939) and of H. Zimmerle (1938) indicates that trees which have been released grow approximately twice as
fast in diameter as trees in the average naturally occurring stand, all
other factors being equal.

Average tree diameter is also a function of stand height. When
tree diameter is plotted against tree height, using Cartesian coordinates (Figure 1), a scatter of points is obtained; however, it is the
task of science to bring about order from this "chaos" and to discover
relationships. The scatter of points in Figure 1 consists of a streak
running diagonally away from a point at or near the origin of the coordinates. This trend leads to the supposition that the mean stand diameter is almost directly proportional to mean stand height, but crowding
variations cause the points to deviate from a straight line.

Determination of Normal Density of Stocking (Crowding)

In order to determine how diameter decreases when crowding increases, a satisfactory measure of stand density must be found. Finding
such a measure is not easy. Obviously it cannot be simply number of
trees per surface unit, because a certain number in a young stand may
represent conditions of unused growing space, while the identical number

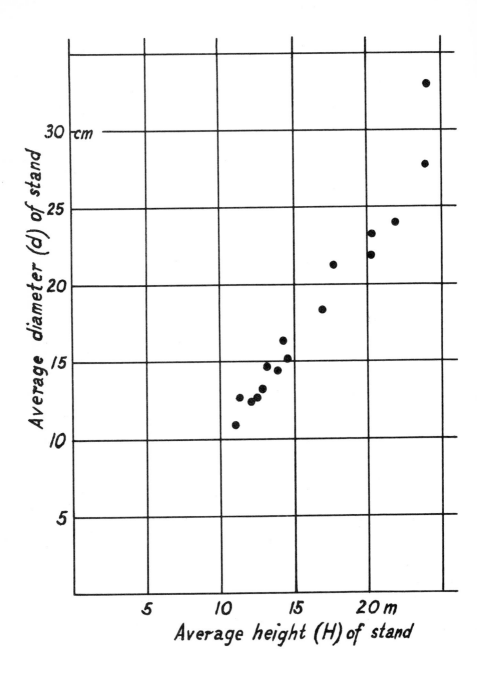

FIGURE 1. Relationship of average height and average diameter in pure, even-aged stands. Each point represents one stand.

in an old stand may represent complete utilization of growing space. Therefore, a measure of crowding must be found that is independent of stand age.

To solve the problem, understanding of some principles of forest biology is necessary.

A tree that grows its whole life in the open has live limbs along the bole extending almost all the way from its tip to ground level. Therefore its crown is as long as its total height. On the other hand, a tree that has grown surrounded by other trees as a member of a forest community has a crown which begins higher up on the bole, often being two-thirds or less as long as the tree height; the trunk is free of branches and dead limbs, particularly in the lower part. The ratio of average live-crown length to average tree height can be regarded as a measure of the degree of crowding of trees in the stand. European Scots pine has a live-crown (or crown-length) ratio commonly averaging one-third (when fully stocked). A Scots pine stand having this average ratio equal to one-third could be called a "normal" one in regard to crowding. In nature such a stand may be encountered only occasionally, but such a concept of normality appears to be instructive and useful in experimental work for understanding the dynamics of forest stands. Crown-length ratio will be further discussed in Chapter VIII.

Relationship between Mean Tree Height and Normal Crowding

In 1947 the author (Czarnowski, 1947b) set forth the following hypothesis: In normal, pure, even-aged stands of a given species growing on land of identical site quality, the number of trees growing on a land area equal to the square of mean stand height is a constant value, independent of stand age.

Because other stand parameters as a rule are expressed on the basis of a conventional surface unit (acre or hectare), it is also convenient to express number of trees as a function of stand height in relation to the same conventional unit. In Figure 2 the larger square of area equal to P represents the conventional surface unit of area and the smaller square (H^2) the surface area equal to the square of mean stand height (H). If on area P there are N trees, on area H^2 there are $\overset{\shortmid}{N}$ trees. Therefore, if the trees are distributed uniformly:

$$\frac{P}{H^2} = \frac{N}{\overset{\shortmid}{N}}$$

$$N = \overset{\shortmid}{N} \frac{P}{H^2} \tag{1}$$

If N is now defined as "normal number of trees per conventional surface unit," the term "normal" meaning that the stand has a certain density determined by the crown-length ratio, then it follows from the above hypothesis that $\overset{\shortmid}{N}$ will be a constant for a given site quality.

Thus the hypothesis provides a way of computing the normal number of trees and thereby expressing crowding in a quantitative way. In other words, the hypothesis enables the expression of the degree of crowding or competition between trees numerically, because this degree may be expressed as the ratio of the actual number of trees per unit of land area to the normal number. This ratio is hereby termed "z" or "crowding" factor. The crowding factor has been defined and discussed by the author in an earlier publication (Czarnowski, 1947a). When z = 1

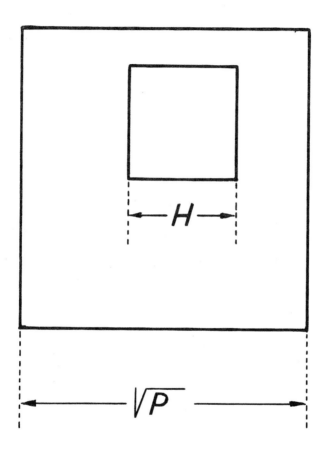

FIGURE 2. Conventional unit of land area (P), containing unit of land area (H^2), where H = average stand height.

for an actual stand, the stand is assumed to be normally stocked.

The author's hypothesis may also be expressed as follows: In pure, even-aged stands of a given species growing on land of identical site quality and under conditions of comparable competition for growing space, the number of trees per unit of land area is inversely proportional to the square of the mean height of the stand.

Relationship between Mean Tree Diameter, Mean Tree Height, and Stand Density

It is customary to measure tree diameter at breast height, which is 54 inches above ground level in the United States (51 inches in Britain and 1.3 meters on the continent of Europe). A tree or stand having a height of exactly 4.5 feet (1.3 meters in Europe) has a diameter breast-high equal to zero. Taking this into account and assuming that the mean diameter growth of open-grown trees is about twice that of the average tree grown in the normally stocked stand, all other things being equal, the following equation may be used to express the relationship of diameter to height and density:

$$d = \alpha (H - X) \frac{2}{z + 1}$$

where

> d = mean stand diameter, measured at a point X feet above ground
>
> α = coefficient of proportionality, which depends on the degree of "compactness" of the stand
>
> H = mean stand height
>
> z = crowding factor, which is the ratio of actual number of trees per unit of land area to the normal number

Equation (2) may be expanded algebraically:

$$d = \alpha H \frac{2}{z + 1} - \alpha \cdot X \frac{2}{z + 1}$$

Since the value of the term $\alpha \cdot X \dfrac{2}{z + 1}$ is very small in comparison

with $\alpha H \dfrac{2}{z + 1}$, the former term may be treated as a constant (Δ) for

a given species. Therefore:

$$d = \alpha H \frac{2}{z + 1} - \Delta \tag{3}$$

These formulas help to explain the cause of the dispersion of

points in Figure 1; the deviations of diameter from the straight-line

relationship with height are associated with variations in stand crowd-

ing.

Results expected from equation (3) may now be compared with ex-

perimental data already collected. This comparison is presented in

Table 3. For the calculation of mean stand diameter by equation (3),

α is assumed to be equal to 0.148 and Δ equals 0.6. The differences in

Table 3 between experimental (presented by Jedliński et al., 1932) and

calculated mean stand diameters are minor, amounting to 2 per cent at

most, and could be due to slight inaccuracies of measurement or minor

errors in computing α, Δ, or z. Taking into consideration the complex-

ity of forest stands, the result obtained must be considered good.

In solving this long unraveled phenomenon of forest composition,

a much-abbreviated and simplified deduction has just been presented.

The solution has been accomplished by the method used in classical

physics -- a method applicable to living creatures, to collections of

trees, and to forest stands. The solution reveals that in pure, even-

aged stands, trees adjust their diameters to the degree of crowding.

TABLE 3. Comparison of formula values of average stand diameter with actual measured values. Formula values were calculated by equation (3). Data are for selected Scots pine stands (from Jedliński et al., 1932).

Age in years	Av. height in feet	Crowding factor	Av. d.b.h. in inches actual	calculated by formula	Difference between actual and calculated diameter, inches
a	H	z	d_a	d_f	$d_f - d_a$
31	36.1	1.18	4.3	4.3	0.0
36	37.1	0.93	5.0	5.1	0.1
44	38.7	1.10	4.9	5.0	0.1
48	41.0	1.18	5.0	5.0	0.0
51	42.3	1.11	5.3	5.3	0.0
42	43.3	1.03	5.8	5.7	-0.1
39	45.5	1.12	5.7	5.7	0.0
67	46.8	1.00	6.4	6.3	-0.1
41	47.8	1.10	6.0	6.1	0.1
43	55.7	1.12	7.2	7.2	0.0
71	61.6	0.94	8.4	8.2	-0.2
75	66.5	1.19	8.6	8.4	-0.2
67	66.5	1.05	9.1	9.1	0.0
59	71.7	1.10	9.4	9.4	0.0
60	78.7	1.00	11.0	11.0	0.0
96	79.0	0.70	13.0	13.1	0.1

Since crowding is controlled in silviculture by thinnings, the known relationship between tree diameter and stand crowding is useful as a tool for the deliberate manipulation of tree size, of course within natural limits expressed by equations.

Chapter II

DISCUSSION OF THE HYPOTHESIS

In the preceding chapter it was explained that in the equation $N = N' \dfrac{P}{H^2}$ the coefficient N' is not merely a formal term; it represents a concrete magnitude. The hypothesis and the equation which is derived from it appear to be logically constructed.

Consider the function $N = f(N', H, P)$. It is obvious that N is directly proportional to P. It is also known that N is inversely proportional to some function of H. If N' is a coefficient of proportionality, it may be imputed to the above function the equation $N = N' \dfrac{P}{H^n}$. To obtain a true equation, the exponent n of H must be exactly equal to 2, because the magnitude P, being an area, is in the second power. Then: $N = N' \dfrac{P}{H^2}$.

The equation is true from a mathematical point of view. But from the natural point of view it is questionable whether the quantity N' is actually constant for a given site quality. To settle the question some long-term observations from stands grown under exactly constant ecological conditions are needed. However, these conditions can never really be exactly constant because natural factors affecting tree growth vary from year to year. Possibly the nearest approach to this ideal data was presented by G. R. Eytingen (1949). In 1862 observations

were begun in a Scots pine stand in the experimental forest of the
School of Agriculture in Moscow. At that time the stand was 18 years
old and had 8391 trees per hectare. Since then there have been no thinnings except for the felling of dead trees. Table 4 shows the observations, and Figure 3 shows the trend in number of trees per hectare.

Attention is called to the fluctuations in the numbers in the
last column of Table 4. These fluctuations are not systematic; therefore we may conclude that they are independent of age. Fluctuations are
quite understandable, since it is known that constancy of ecological
conditions in these circumstances is impossible. However, independence
of stand age of these fluctuations is sufficient confirmation of the hypothesis.

Some useful experimental material is no doubt contained in normal yield tables. However, yield tables contain data which are mean or
smoothed-out values from a number of observations of stands grown in
different ecological conditions; therefore these data are to some extent
modified by the smoothing or averaging process. Using yield-table data
one also obtains results which agree closely with the hypothesis. Figure 4 shows the comparison of data taken from normal yield tables for
Scots pine presented by W. Płoński (1937) with numbers calculated by use
of formula (1).

The hypothesis discussed above is logical, mathematically valid,
and confirmed by a scientific experiment performed under natural conditions. The next tasks to be undertaken in this field of ecological
science are:

1. To constitute the smallest possible number of the simplest

TABLE 4. Observations in an unthinned Scots pine stand near Moscow,
U.S.S.R. (from Eytingen, 1949).

Year	Age a (years)	Number of trees per hectare N	Height H (meters)	Diameter b.h. d (centimeters)	Actual number of trees on the surface equal to H² N'
1862	18	8391	-	-	-
1888	43	1378	19.2	17.6	50.8
1904	59	939	25.0	23.2	58.7
1915	70	675	27.9	26.5	52.3
1921	76	599	29.9	28.0	53.5
1937	92	489	32.0	30.0	50.2

possible hypotheses sufficient to describe with the greatest possible
accuracy and thoroughness, by the use of logical deduction, the nature
of the phenomena that will appear when the predicted conditions are realized (of course within certain limits of accuracy).

2. To determine the most important logical consequences of
these hypotheses.

A primary problem is that of the measurement of elements represented in the field of our interest. Thus the task is to specify the
general conventions which represent certain numbers, which shall be
called "indices." To define the index of any element represented in nature is difficult, but such a definition is to some degree a matter of
convention, not bound by unbreakable principles. It is desirable and
even necessary to devise such a definition or to formulate a hypothesis
such that the mathematical formulas following from it will be presented
in forms as simple and clear as possible, and also as accurate and ex-
haustive as necessary.

Therefore the questions must be answered from the point of view
of the logical consequences of the hypothesis. As is known already, the

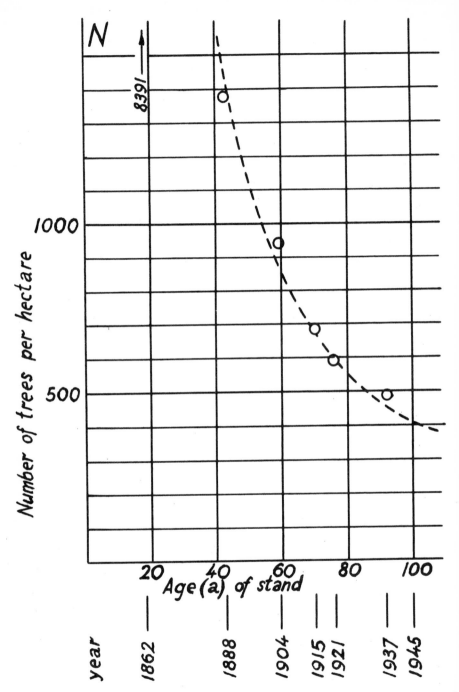

FIGURE 3. Number of trees per hectare at various ages during the life of an unthinned Scots pine stand.

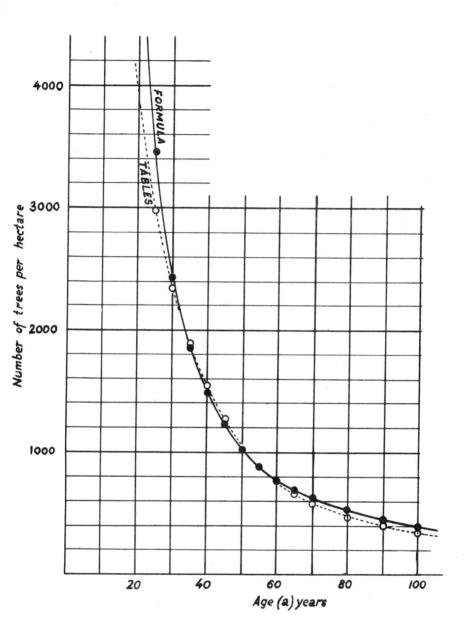

FIGURE 4. Number of trees per hectare for Scots pine stands at various ages. Płoński's yield table values for site class Ia (dashed line) compared to values calculated by formula (1) using N̂ = 42 (solid line).

hypothesis enables creation of an index of crowding, expressed as a
ratio:

$$z = \frac{\text{actual number of trees per surface unit P}}{\text{normal number of trees per surface unit P}} = \frac{N_r}{N}$$

where N is calculated using formula (1), or:

$$z = \frac{\text{actual number of trees per surface equal to } H^2}{\text{normal number of trees per surface equal to } H^2} = \frac{N_r'}{N}$$

Reminder is made that z is an abstract number; it is represented
in the formula already presented [equations (2) and (3)]:

$$d = \alpha (H - X) \frac{2}{z+1} = \alpha H \frac{2}{z+1} - \Delta$$

Therefore, the investigation of the validity of the hypothesis means
testing for conformity of the consequences of the hypothesis (for example, the last formula) with experimental data and with previously veri-
fied scientific generalizations. The testing of formula (2) against
experimental data will be shown in Chapter V, Tables 13 and 14. For the
present, comparison is made of the consequences of the hypothesis with
the most important scientific generalizations already expounded in our
field of interest.

Comparison of the Hypothesis with Köhler's Generalization

First, attention is called to a verbal generalization of Köhler
(Tkachenko, 1939; Wilson, 1946): The area occupied by a living tree in
normal stands of Scots pine is equal to the square of 1/6 the tree
height, regardless of age. The generalization may be expressed mathematically. Thus when the tree area is represented by the symbol Y, then

the number of trees per surface unit P will be:

$$N = \frac{P}{Y}$$

According to Köhler's opinion:

$$Y = \left(\frac{1}{6} \cdot H \right)^2$$

thus

$$N = 36 \frac{P}{H^2}$$

In this way a formula is obtained which is identical in construction with formula (1), and the number 36 corresponds to our site indicator $\overset{\text{'}}{N}$ But of course Köhler's number 36 is only a first approximation, because the site indicator $\overset{\text{'}}{N}$ is not a fixed value in different localities but depends on the productive capacity of the locality. For instance, in Polish Scots pine stands the values of this indicator $\overset{\text{'}}{N}$, expressed as mean values from data for 30- to 100-year-old stands, are as follows:

Site class (Płoński, 1937)	Mean height at the age of 50 years in feet	$\overset{\text{'}}{N}$	Coefficient of variation
Ia	66	41.0	$\pm$ 4.4%
I	55	39.2	$\pm$ 4.4%
II	52	35.2	$\pm$ 4.5%
III	45	31.6	$\pm$ 4.3%
IV	38	28.6	$\pm$ 4.3%
V	31	22.3	$\pm$ 3.9%
Va	24	17.2	$\pm$ 3.6%

Although Köhler's generalization is exactly correct only when $\overset{\text{'}}{N} = 36$ (Płoński's site class II), the construction of the above formula, deduced from it, is in complete agreement with formula (1).

For loblolly pine (Pinus taeda L.) in Louisiana (see Chapter

IV), the author found values of $\overset{\text{'}}{N}$ to be as follows:

Site index (height of dominant trees at the age of 50 years in feet)	Site indicator $\overset{\text{'}}{N}$
120	38.0
110	35.9
100	34.2
90	32.8
80	31.2
70	29.5
60	27.4

Comparison of the Hypothesis with Khil'mi's Theory

In 1955 G. F. Khil'mi in a lengthy work using the theory of sim-

ilitude (which was so fruitfully applied in mechanics) concluded that

between the stand height and the number of trees per surface unit there

exists the relationship:

$$H = \frac{R}{\sqrt{N}}$$

where R is a coefficient of proportionality depending on the productive

capacity of the locality.

Thus:

$$N = \frac{R^2}{H^2}$$

Khil'mi remarked that when productive capacity of locality diminishes,

the values of R diminish also. Thus we find evidence of conformity of

his results with formula (1).

Comparison of the Hypothesis with Chisman and Schumacher's Tree-area Ratio

In 1940 H. H. Chisman and F. X. Schumacher, working in the United States, presented the formula:

$$Y = b_2 \cdot d^2 + b_1 \cdot d + b_0$$

where:

Y = tree area

d = diameter b.h.

b_2, b_1, b_0 = coefficients

A comparison of this formula is made with formulas (1) and (2).

When:

$$Y = \frac{P}{N}$$

then:

$$Y = \frac{P}{N' \dfrac{P}{H^2}}$$

thus:

$$Y = \frac{H^2}{N'}$$

From Formula (2) the relationship is obtained:

$$d + \Delta = \alpha \cdot H \frac{2}{z + 1}$$

Then solving for H:

$$H = \frac{d\,(z+1)}{2\,\alpha} + \frac{\Delta\,(z+1)}{2\,\alpha}$$

and squaring:

$$H^2 = \frac{d^2 \cdot (z+1)^2}{4 \cdot \alpha^2} + \frac{2 \cdot d \cdot \Delta\,(z+1)^2}{4 \cdot \alpha^2} + \frac{\Delta^2 \cdot (z+1)^2}{4 \cdot \alpha^2}$$

dividing by $\overset{\text{'}}{N}$ and substituting:

$$Y = \frac{(z+1)^2}{4 \cdot a^2 \cdot \overset{\text{'}}{N}} d^2 + \frac{2 \cdot \Delta (z+1)^2}{4 \cdot a^2 \cdot \overset{\text{'}}{N}} d + \frac{\Delta^2 \cdot (z+1)^2}{4 \cdot a^2 \cdot \overset{\text{'}}{N}}$$

The similarity of these results with Chisman and Schumacher's formula is evident, but that is not the end of the matter. From the theory which included formulas (1) and (2) the following equation is derived:

$$b_1 = 2 \sqrt{b_2 \cdot b_o}$$

If the formula of Chisman and Schumacher is a particular case of more general formulas deduced from my theory, then the last relationship must exist also in Chisman and Schumacher's formula. These authors give numerical values for loblolly pine, namely:

$$b_2 = 0.0267$$

$$b_o = 0.0460$$

$$b_1 = 0.0668$$

It may be calculated:

$$b_1 = 2 \sqrt{(0.0267)(0.0460)} = 0.070$$

while according to the authors:

$$b_1 = 0.0668$$

Between Chisman and Schumacher's formula and the result based on the theory of stand dynamics there is close agreement; besides, the theory enables the expression in a more detailed way of the mean area for one tree in a stand and expression of the existing relations by means of coefficients that more clearly show the nature of the subject, namely:

$$Y = \left(\frac{z + 1}{2 \cdot a} \right)^2 \frac{1}{\overset{\text{'}}{N}} (d + \Delta)^2$$

Comparison of the Hypothesis with Bistrup's Formula

In 1951 C. Bistrup published the formula (in the metric system) applicable to normal beech stands:

$$N = \frac{10,000}{(A_1 + B_1 \cdot d)^2}$$

Formula (1) in the metric system is as follows:

$$N = N' \frac{10,000}{H^2}$$

or

$$N = \frac{10,000}{\dfrac{H^2}{N'}}$$

When z = 1, as shown in formula (2):

$$H^2 = \left(\frac{d}{\alpha} + \frac{\Delta}{\alpha} \right)^2$$

Thus:

$$\frac{H^2}{N'} = \left(\frac{d}{\alpha\sqrt{N'}} + \frac{\Delta}{\alpha\sqrt{N'}} \right)^2$$

Therefore:

$$N = \frac{10,000}{\left(\dfrac{d}{\alpha\sqrt{N'}} + \dfrac{\Delta}{\alpha\sqrt{N'}} \right)^2}$$

In Bistrup's formula:

$$\frac{\Delta}{\alpha\sqrt{N'}} = A_1$$

$$\frac{1}{\alpha\sqrt{N'}} = B_1$$

Bistrup's A_1 is equal to Chisman and Schumacher's $\sqrt{b_0}$, and Bistrup's B_1 is equal to Chisman and Schumacher's $\sqrt{b_2}$ (of course when z = 1).

The theory of stand dynamics herein presented explains exhaustively the mechanism of coordination of stand characteristics, so that separate generalizations concerning stand dynamics which are made independently by different authors appear to be only particular cases of formulas (1) and (2). The above analysis shows the relationship of the elements to this author's general hypothesis.

Chapter III

HEIGHT GROWTH AND THE PRODUCTIVE CAPACITY

OF THE LOCALITY (SITE QUALITY)

As has been seen in the preceding chapter, the magnitude $\overset{\shortmid}{N}$ is a function of the productive capacity of the locality. Thus this magnitude may be used as an index of this capacity -- a "site indicator." Therefore this indicator must be a function of the height of the stand as well as of the height growth. Thus:

$$\overset{\shortmid}{N} = f(h)$$

where:

h = mean annual stand height growth at an age a.

The course of development of stand height is not a new problem in forestry. In 1891 R. Weber published the formula:

$$H = H_{max} \left(1 - \frac{1}{p^a} \right)$$

After its improvement by A. V. Tyurin (1928) this formula read as follows:

$$H = H_{max} \left(1 - \frac{1}{p^{a-b}} \right)$$

where:

H = height of the dominant class of trees in the stand

a = age

H_{max} = maximum obtainable height of stand in the definite locality, a magnitude fluctuating in Scots pine stands
from 43.0 meters (the best site class) to 15.5 meters
(the lowest site class)

p = constant for the species

b = magnitude, fluctuating in Scots pine stands from 4 (the
best site class) to 10 (the lowest site class)

Although Weber-Tyurin's formula among other proposals gives good

results, its form is not true because of the following facts:

1. The function has no point of inflection, although in nature

the curve of height over age has this point at the age of height-growth

culmination.

2. The derivative of the Weber-Tyurin function with respect to

age a is a function which constantly diminishes within the limits from

0 to $+\infty$, while the derivative of a function which demonstrates the nat-

ural course of height (thus the course of height growth) has the values:

Age a	Value of height-growth
0	0
$+\infty > a > 0$	maximum
$a \rightarrow +\infty$	$\rightarrow 0$

Moreover, in Weber-Tyurin's formula the postulate of limiting

values of H_{max} is doubtful. Whether tree height at a great age repre-

sents a limited or an infinite value is an unsettled question. Trees

grow until death in thickness and probably in height. In nature it fre-

quently happens that in the old age of a tree a calamity (lightning-

strike, hurricane, fire) or an invasion of insects breaks off its life.

Some exceptionally aged trees grow incessantly and reach impressively

huge sizes. These trees, to be sure, fade away in growth (particularly in height growth) and show serious damages by winds, frosts, and so forth, which constantly reduce the achieved growth and force the living organism to a constant regeneration. Nevertheless, it is just this regeneration capacity which gives evidence that the tree is potentially predestined to accomplish its height growth regardless of its age. In the animal kingdom, particularly in classes of highly organized mammals, there exist indeed some limited values of dimensions, such as length of body. In herbaceous plants which are predestined to accomplish their physiological functions in one year, there are perhaps some limited values. But trees are not limited to the accomplishment of their physiological functions in a definite number of years; thus the diminution of height growth does not impose on the tree any height limit. Because of these considerations there seems to be no reason to impute the existence of any limit to tree height.

The phenomenon of the height growth of the tree must be treated in quite another way. During its first years the tree grows slowly in height, but growth increases every year up to a certain maximal value; afterwards, growth diminishes rather suddenly for a few years and then fades constantly and gently. Thus it may be said figuratively that the greater growth the tree has yet to make, the faster it grows; but at the same time, the greater size the tree has already reached, the slower it grows. Here two tendencies act, the resultant of which gives the course of height growth.

The "fading power" acts intensively during the tree's youth, diminishing constantly towards zero, attains the value of zero at a certain age, and afterwards slowly increases, constantly repressing the

growth. If the growth were a constant value, the image of it on Cartesian coordinates would be a straight line running through the origin of
the coordinates. But because there acts a power which is the resultant
of two contradictory tendencies, the course of growth appears as a more
complicated phenomenon.

By the symbol h_A is expressed this imaginary growth that would
exist if no fading nor protective power were acting, and by the symbol
h is expressed the normal growth at age a, i.e. the growth that would
exist if the weather during each year were the same. Then h is an outcome of the action of the resultant on h_A. In mathematical language:

$$h = h_A - f_I(a)$$

Since $f_I(a)$ is proportional to h_A (in the more productive locality the
resultant acts more intensively than in the less productive one), one
may suppose that:

$$h = h_A - h_A \cdot f_{II}(a)$$

or:

$$h = h_A \left[1 - f_{II}(a) \right]$$

As is already known, at a certain age $f_{II}(a) = 0$. This age is designated A. At this age the growth is equal to h_A. As the fading power is a
resultant of two tendencies, it seems to be possible that:

$$f_{II}(a) = \frac{f_{III}(a)}{f_{IV}(a)}$$

Examine Figure 5, which presents the picture of height growth. Compare
this picture with the equation:

$$h = h_A \cdot \left[1 - \frac{f_{III}(a)}{f_{IV}(a)} \right]$$

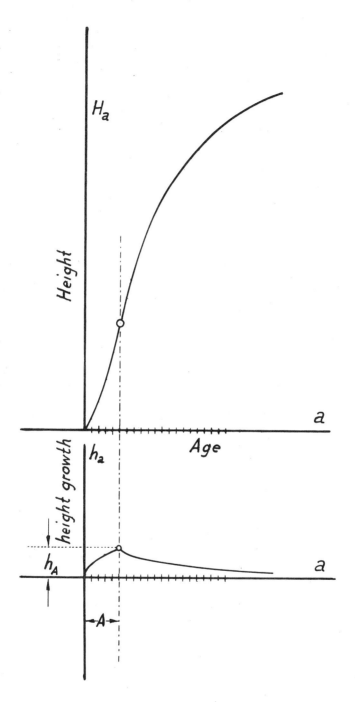

FIGURE 5. The normal curve of tree height (above) and the theoretical curve of tree height growth (below).

There are seen the following relationships:

a	$\dfrac{f_{III}(a)}{f_{IV}(a)}$
0	1
$<A$	<1
A	0
$>A$	<1
$\rightarrow +\infty$	$\rightarrow 1$

This indicates that the function $f_{III}(a)$ is rather the function of the difference $(A - a)$, not of only a. The action is similar on both sides towards the point of culmination; therefore it is legitimate to impute the equation:

$$h = h_A \left\{ 1 - \frac{f_V\left(|A - a|\right)}{f_{IV}(a)} \right\}$$

As at the age $a = 0$, the value of $h = 0$, then the magnitude A must be represented also in the function $f_{IV}(a)$. Thus, finally is imputed to the phenomenon the equation:

$$h = h_A \left\{ 1 - \left| \frac{a - A}{a + A} \right| \right\} \tag{5}$$

Integrating this function with respect to a and for the values $a \leq A$ the following is obtained:

$$\int_0^a h \cdot da = H = 2 \cdot h_A \left\{ a - A \cdot \ln\left(1 + \frac{a}{A}\right) \right\} \tag{6}$$

and for the values $a \geq A$:

$$\int_0^a h \cdot da = H = 2 \cdot A \cdot h_A \cdot \left\{ 1 - \ln 4 + \ln\left(1 + \frac{a}{A}\right) \right\}$$

$$H = 2 \cdot A \cdot h_A \cdot \left\{ \ln\left(1 + \frac{a}{A}\right) - 0.386 \right\} \tag{7}$$

Here "ln" means the natural logarithm.

From the last formula it arises that for definite sites there are definite values of A and h_A. This agrees with the usual views about the significance of the site. To show how this equation works, the following comparison is given between data taken from normal yield tables for Scots pine stands, site class IV (Płoński, 1937) and the results obtained by the last formula ($N' = 26$, $A = 20$, $h_A = 0.355$ m.):

Age (a) in years	Mean height of stand (H) in meters	
	experimental	calculated
30	7.6	7.1
40	9.7	9.6
50	11.6	11.6
60	13.4	13.4
70	14.9	15.0
80	16.3	16.3
90	17.5	17.7
100	18.5	18.8

In all the other site classes striking agreements (see Table 5) have also been obtained. Notwithstanding the existence of these agreements, there still remain some problems concerning the form of the author's equation. The first one is whether or not the term $\left| \dfrac{A - a}{A + a} \right|$ is in fact exactly in the first power. The theoretical results show that the curve of height growth for an individual tree is a line that is sharply broken at the maximum point (see Figure 5), while the curves (for stands) that are presented in the literature, for instance by Guttenberg (taken from Vanselow, 1941), have a very smooth course (see Figure 6). This situation is easy to explain: the curves given in the literature present the course of average values for trees existing in one stand, but which are by no means in the same condition with regard to the age of culmination of the height growth. If in a stand $\dfrac{1}{3}$ of

TABLE 5. Comparison of experimental heights from Płoński's (1937) yield tables for Scots pine with heights obtained by using formula (7a).

Płoński's site class	Ia		I		II		III		IV		V	
N	→ 41.0		39.2		35.2		31.6		26.8		22.3	
A (yrs.)	→ 16.75		18.4		18.8		19.87		20.0		20.5	
h_A (meters)	→ 0.612		0.532		0.468		0.399		0.335		0.272	
$a_\downarrow$ (yrs.)	exp.	calc.	exp.	calc.	exp.	calc.	exp.	calc.	exp.	calc.	exp.	calc.
	Heights (H) of stands in meters											
30	13.1	12.8	11.7	11.0	10.3	9.7	8.9	8.2	7.6	7.1	6.2	5.5
40	16.8	16.8	15.0	14.7	13.2	13.0	11.5	11.1	9.7	9.6	7.9	7.6
50	20.2	20.1	18.0	17.8	15.9	15.7	13.8	13.5	11.6	11.6	9.5	9.3
60	23.2	22.9	20.8	20.5	18.3	18.1	15.8	15.6	13.4	13.4	10.9	10.7
70	25.9	25.5	23.2	22.9	20.4	20.2	17.7	17.5	14.9	15.0	12.2	12.2
80	28.3	27.7	25.3	25.0	22.3	22.1	19.3	19.1	16.3	16.3	13.3	13.2
90	30.4	29.8	27.2	26.8	23.9	23.8	20.7	20.6	17.5	17.7	14.3	14.3
100	32.1	31.6	28.7	28.6	25.3	25.3	21.9	21.9	18.5	18.8	15.1	15.2

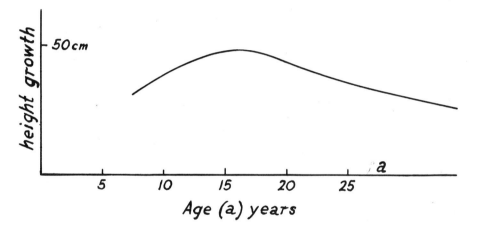

FIGURE 6. The experimental curve of stand height growth presented by Guttenberg (from Vanselow, 1941).

the total number of trees culminate their height growth at the age of 15

years, $\frac{1}{3}$ at the age of 16 years, and $\frac{1}{3}$ at the age of 17 years, then

the function

$$f_x(a) = \frac{1}{3}\left[\left(1 - \left|\frac{a - 15}{a + 15}\right|\right) + \left(1 - \left|\frac{a - 16}{a + 16}\right|\right) + \left(1 - \left|\frac{a - 17}{a + 17}\right|\right)\right]$$

will give a smooth line in the field of culmination which appears at the

age of 16 years (see Figure 7).

If it is assumed that:

$$h_a = h_A \cdot \left[1 - \left(\left|\frac{a - A}{a + A}\right|\right)^n\right]$$

the value of n may be calculated:

$$n = \frac{\log\left(1 - \frac{h_a}{h_A}\right)}{\log\left(\left|\frac{a - A}{a + A}\right|\right)}$$

(5

where h_a is the mean value obtained by measurements and where A is to be

computed by means of the method of substitution from the formula:

$$\frac{H_1}{H_2} = \frac{\ln\left(1 + \frac{a_1}{A}\right) - 0.3863}{\ln\left(1 + \frac{a_2}{A}\right) - 0.3863}$$

and h_A from the formula:

$$h_A = \frac{H_1}{2 \cdot A \cdot \left\{\ln\left(1 + \frac{a_1}{A}\right) - 0.3863\right\}}$$

(5

where H_1, H_2, a_1, a_2 are the experimental values. In this way for a

Scots pine stand near Cracow, Poland, the author has obtained, for the

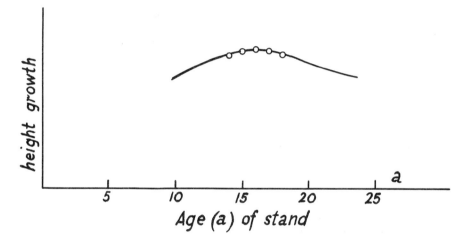

FIGURE 7. The theoretical curve of stand height growth, when the ages of culmination of growth differ for individual trees in the stand.

period from age 13 to age 44, the mean value (Table 6):

$$n = 1.016$$

Therefore, it may be considered that the true value of the exponent is equal to 1.

The second question is the problem of the relation between the magnitudes $A \cdot h_A$ and the magnitude $\overset{\shortmid}{N}$. For Scots pine stands it is found that:

$$A \cdot h_A = C_\bullet \cdot \overset{\shortmid}{N}$$

where for Scots pine $C_\bullet$ is a constant value. In the metrical system:

$$A \cdot h_A = 0.25 \cdot \overset{\shortmid}{N}$$

thus:

$$h_A = \frac{0.25}{A} \overset{\shortmid}{N}$$

Finally, for Scots pine stands in the metrical system is obtained the formula (when $a > A$):

$$H = C_* \overset{\shortmid}{N} \left\{ \ln \left(1 + \frac{a}{A} \right) - 0.386 \right\}$$

where for Scots pine stands $C_* = 0.5$.

The magnitude A is also a function of $\overset{\shortmid}{N}$, but it varies only slightly and is confined within limits from 17 to 20 years in Scots pine stands. Therefore, using this formula one may calculate the value of $\overset{\shortmid}{N}$, knowing the value of H and a and estimating the value of A. Of course in practice one need not do any calculations, as appropriate nomograms (as for instance Figure 8) can be used.

In Norway spruce stands in Poland the author has observed that the term $C_* = C_s \cdot (1 - c_o \cdot a)$, where C_s and c_o are constant values and where c_o is a very small value, but > 0. Thus it is possible that the

TABLE 6.   Calculation of the mean value of the exponent n in formula (5a).   Data are for a Scots pine stand near Cracow, Poland.   Height growth is an average of 15 dominant trees as determined by internode measurements.   A = 18 years.

Age a (years)	Actual height growth h_a (cm.)	$n = \dfrac{\lg \left(1 - \dfrac{h_a}{h_A}\right)}{\lg \left\| \dfrac{A - a}{A + a} \right\|}$
13	60.8	1.147
14	67.1	1.655
15	68.8	2.070
16	67.4	1.276
17	65.5	0.811
18	68.1	-
19	67.4	1.000
20	69.3	-
21	63.9	0.995
22	61.8	0.966
23	53.5	0.703
24	52.9	0.740
25	63.3	1.346
26	54.7	0.913
27	60.1	1.253
28	61.4	1.426
29	54.9	1.081
30	52.3	1.014
31	53.3	1.103
32	50.5	1.026
33	51.9	1.132
34	50.8	1.121
35	42.0	0.820
36	41.3	0.824
37	33.2	0.613
38	27.4	0.488
39	33.4	0.658
40	39.2	0.860
41	39.4	0.891
42	31.5	0.881
43	30.5	0.650
44	38.4	0.928

Total of 30 values = 30.480

Mean n = 30.480/30 = 1.016 ≈ 1.0

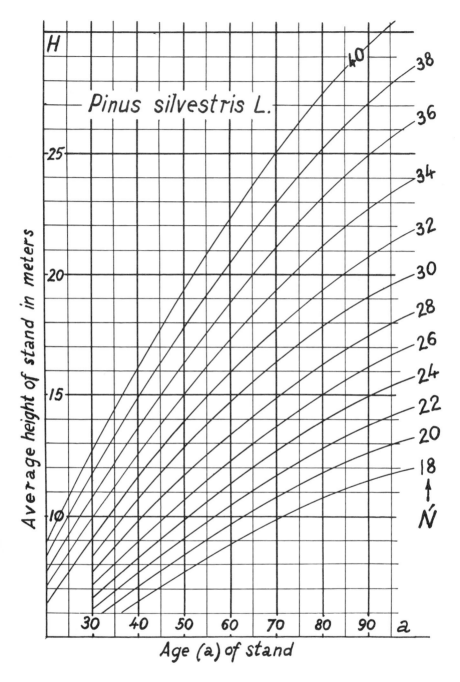

FIGURE 8. Stand height as a function of age (a) and site indicator (Ń) for Scots pine in Poland.

formula for Scots pine stands is a particular case (when for instance c_o = 0) of a more general equation that may be elaborated in the future, based on material concerning other species.

Here is another important question. Textbooks of silviculture state that the number of trees per surface unit diminishes (hyperbolically) as the age increases and that for the same age this number increases as the site quality diminishes. Consider this strongly founded observation from the viewpoint of results based on the hypothesis presented:

$$N = N' \frac{P}{H^2} \tag{1}$$

where the magnitude H may be expressed as a function of the magnitude N' (formula 7a); thus:

$$N = \frac{N' \cdot P}{\left\{ c_* \cdot N' \left[\ln \left(1 + \frac{a}{A} \right) - 0.3863 \right] \right\}^2}$$

then

$$N = \frac{P}{N' \cdot \left\{ c_* \cdot \left[\ln \left(1 + \frac{a}{A} \right) - 0.3863 \right] \right\}^2} \tag{9}$$

As a matter of course an important result has been obtained which agrees plainly with the above-mentioned basic observation, until now expressed only in words. Here again there is complete agreement of the presented hypothesis with a duly founded generalization in the field of stand dynamics.

Chapter IV

DETERMINATION OF MAXIMUM VOLUME PER UNIT OF LAND AREA

In this chapter an approach will be made to the solving of the problem of maximum attainable volume per surface unit by means of the author's theory, which in brief contains two hypotheses:

1. In pure, even-aged stands in a definite locality and grown under definite ecological conditions the number of trees per surface unit is inversely proportional to the square of the mean height of the stand.

2. The average diameter breast high in a stand is directly proportional to the mean stand height reduced by the height of measurement of diameter (1.3 meters or 4.5 feet) and inversely proportional to the crowding factor enlarged by the value 1.

Thus:

$$d = \alpha (H - X) \frac{2}{z+1} \eqsim \alpha H \frac{2}{z+1} - \Delta$$

where:

d = average stand diameter, measured at a height X from the ground level

α = coefficient of proportionality, constant for a species and for given stand intensity and site

H = mean stand height

z = crowding factor = $\dfrac{\text{actual number of trees per surface unit}}{\text{normal number of trees per surface unit}} = \dfrac{N_r}{N}$

40

$$\frac{M}{H} = \text{stand intensity}$$

M = volume of wood per unit of land area

Δ = constant for a species

From the first hypothesis:

$$N = \overset{\shortmid}{N} \frac{P}{H^2} \qquad (1)$$

where $\overset{\shortmid}{N}$ is a constant value for the definite locality and ecological conditions and is independent of the system of measurement. In the metric system (when H is measured in meters and N is expressed per hectare):

$$P = 100^2$$

In the system customary in the United States (when H is in feet and N per acre):

$$P = 43,560$$

In this chapter the numerical values will refer to the metric system.

The coefficient of proportionality $\overset{\shortmid}{N}$ in formula (1) appears to be a perfect index of the potential productive capacity of the locality or site. This site indicator $\overset{\shortmid}{N}$ acts also as a factor in the relationships:

$$H = C_* \overset{\shortmid}{N} \left\{ \ln \left(1 + \frac{a}{A}\right) - 0.386 \right\} \qquad (7a)$$

where H means a number of length units of the height of stand, and $a \geq A$, and:

$$\alpha = c \sqrt{\frac{M}{H \cdot \overset{\shortmid}{N}}} \qquad (10)$$

where

a = age of the stand (number of years)

A = age of the culmination of stand height growth

M = wood volume per surface unit

C = constant for the species

Thus from formula (3) using formula (10) one obtains:

$$d = c \sqrt{\frac{M}{H \cdot N'}} \, H \, \frac{2}{(z + 1)} - \Delta \qquad (3$$

Using the experimental data presented by W. Weise (1880) (Table 7) the author has calculated the value of the coefficient c using formula (3a) for 270 Scots pine stands, ranging in age from 30 to 100 years, and has obtained the mean value:

$$c = \frac{d + \Delta}{\sqrt{\frac{M}{H \cdot N'}} \, H \, \frac{2}{z + 1}}$$

c = 0.0166

with the coefficient of variation $\pm$ 4.85 per cent.

As is known, the dispersion of diameter values of the separate trees in a compact forest stand represents an average value of at least $\pm$ 25 to $\pm$ 30 per cent in relation to the mean diameter in this stand. Of course this dispersion originates chiefly from the natural differentiation of living individuals in a community, primarily from genetic and microclimatic differences. On the other hand, the dispersion of the separate average diameters of many stands that have the same value of a, H, N, and M amounts scarcely to $\pm$ 5 per cent. What is the cause of this small but still existing dispersion? No doubt it is a consequence of the errors of observations as well as of treating the now-known value z as if this value were constant during the whole life of the stand, which it is not. Some stands in former periods have had z greater than they

TABLE 7. Excerpts of the calculation of the coefficients α and Π for Scots pine stands. Basic data from Weise (1880) for 270 plots in Germany. Δ = 0.6 in. = 1.7 cm. (The coefficient Π will be explained later).

Current plot #	Orig. plot #	Age a	Height H (meters)	Site indicator $\sqrt{N}$	Vol.(M) H·N	Crowding factor z	d.b.h. d (cm.)	$\alpha = \dfrac{(d+\Delta)(z+1)}{H\ 2}$	$\Pi = \alpha\sqrt[4]{\dfrac{1}{N}}$
1	40	123	30.3	38.5	0.770	1.00	41.2	0.0142	0.0354
2	101	97	31.3	40.4	0.638	1.21	38.7	0.0143	0.0361
3	142	83	27.3	39.2	0.670	1.05	34.9	0.0137	0.0342
4	216	63	24.2	41.5	0.604	1.39	26.9	0.0141	0.0358
5	291	46	16.7	38.5	0.730	1.67	16.5	0.0145	0.0361
266	118	90	13.0	20.7	0.743	1.25	14.8	0.0142	0.0303
267	165	78	9.4	16.0	1.290	1.48	11.8	0.0178	0.0356
268	157	79	12.1	20.8	0.717	1.08	14.2	0.0137	0.0292
269	244	57	7.3	17.9	1.200	1.55	8.1	0.0171	0.0352
270	274	50	8.5	20.3	0.783	0.84	11.0	0.0137	0.0291

have today; others have had z smaller. Thus when the mean value of c is calculated from a large number of stands, it is assumed that in this large number the errors springing from this vacillation will be eliminated, and in the result shall be obtained a mean value for c which will be near to the true one.

In order to verify this supposition a series of stands should be used that have been kept in a definite condition of crowding (i.e., when z = constant) during the whole life of each stand. The nearest approach to this material is what was presented by M. Kunze (1918). His was a series of 22 Scots pine stands, each of which had been maintained almost from its origin to the age of about 50 years in certain, almost constant, ecological conditions. Each stand was kept in different crowding conditions (namely, some stands in the crowding condition $z<1$, one in the density $z = 0.7$, others in $z>1$, and one in $z = 1.24$).

Table 8 gives the results obtained by testing formula (3a) against Kunze's data, using the value c = 0.0166. The coefficient of variation for these 22 observations amounts to $\pm$ 1.87 per cent, which is 2.5 times less than the error obtained from the material that showed greater fluctuations of the value of the crowding factor in the former periods of life.

In this series of 22 stands the greatest deviation between the calculated diameter and the experimental diameter amounts to + 4.2 per cent. However, still greater deviations between observed experimental data and duly based formulas may be encountered even in mechanics.

Thus is seen that the cause of these deviations is first of all the error of the assumption of the present-day value of the factor z.

TABLE 8.   Comparison of experimental and calculated values of average diameter using material presented by Kunze (1918) concerning Scots pine in Germany.   Diameters calculated by use of formula (3a).

Plot #	Age a (yrs.)	Actual no. trees per ha. N	Wood vol. per ha. M (cu. m.)	Height H (meters)	Site indicator N	Crowding factor z	Av. d.b.h. (cm.) exp.	Av. d.b.h. (cm.) calc.
1	52	1370	359.6	18.7	38.5	1.16	18.9	18.9
2	52	1370	391.1	19.0	39.2	1.25	19.5	18.9
3	52	1305	343.9	18.7	38.5	1.22	18.6	17.9
4	52	1200	422.3	20.56	40.6	1.25	21.1	20.2
5	52	1012	385.1	19.62	39.7	0.97	21.8	21.7
6	52	1073	427.6	20.25	40.5	1.09	22.2	21.6
7	52	1203	376.2	19.21	38.1	1.12	20.5	20.1
8	52	875	345.7	19.26	38.1	0.82	22.5	22.6
9	50	1435	296.4	16.24	36.0	1.06	17.0	17.1
10	50	1406	323.4	17.28	35.3	1.12	18.1	18.2
11	50	1157	329.0	18.44	38.7	0.99	20.0	19.4
12	51	1615	279.0	14.91	33.4	1.07	16.6	16.3
13	51	1348	290.0	15.62	34.5	0.95	17.9	17.9
14	51	1558	318.6	15.46	34.2	1.09	17.6	17.5
15	51	1240	323.5	16.45	36.0	0.93	19.4	19.3
16	51	1149	304.7	16.04	35.1	0.84	19.8	19.6
17	51	1232	311.3	15.18	34.0	0.85	19.4	19.5
18	51	1312	279.1	14.65	33.0	0.86	18.0	18.2
19	51	976	294.8	15.81	34.8	0.70	20.4	20.7
20	50	1652	290.7	14.65	33.3	1.07	16.9	16.6
21	50	1294	296.7	16.07	35.7	0.95	18.9	18.1
22	50	1326	337.8	16.80	36.7	1.04	19.0	18.7

Summing up: Formulas (2) and (4) can be treated as sufficiently confirmed, at least for Scots pine stands.

Analysis of Table 7 shows that, as the coefficient a increases, the value of the site indicator diminishes. This phenomenon may be observed when Weise's whole numerical material is divided into classes that include values of N from 22.0 to 22.9, from 23.0 to 23.9, and so on (Table 9). A relation may now be imputed:

$$a \sqrt[4]{N} = \Pi \tag{11}$$

TABLE 9.   Relationship between α and N in Scots pine stands and test of formula (11).   Data condensed from Table 7. Π = 0.0309.

Number of observations in the class	Mean value in the class		Calculated value of $\alpha = \dfrac{0.0309}{\sqrt[4]{N}}$
	N	α	
7	22.4	0.01532	0.01420
2	23.4	0.01460	0.01404
2	24.7	0.01400	0.01386
4	25.2	0.01395	0.01378
7	26.1	0.01374	0.01366
9	27.4	0.01351	0.01351
11	28.3	0.01366	0.01339
6	29.4	0.01328	0.01324
8	30.4	0.01287	0.01315
15	31.4	0.01248	0.01306
12	32.3	0.01246	0.01295
14	33.6	0.01285	0.01284
27	34.3	0.01264	0.01276
24	35.3	0.01242	0.01267
29	36.4	0.01254	0.01258
31	37.2	0.01263	0.01251
21	38.4	0.01260	0.01241
17	39.2	0.01212	0.01234

or more generally:

$$\alpha N^{\frac{w}{2}} \approx \Pi \tag{1}$$

where:

Π = constant for a given species

w = constant for a given species

The value of Π for Scots pine was calculated from Weise's data to be 0.0309, with a standard deviation of $\pm$ 0.002232 (Table 7).   This observation enables a more detailed equation to be formed:

$$d = c \, \frac{1}{\sqrt[4]{N}} \, \sqrt{\frac{M}{H \cdot \sqrt{N}}} \, (H - X) \, \frac{2}{z + 1} \tag{1}$$

or

$$d = c \sqrt{\frac{M}{N' \cdot H}} \, (H - X) \, \frac{2}{z + 1} \tag{12a}$$

or still better:

$$d = \Pi \, \frac{1}{\sqrt[4]{N'}} \sqrt{\frac{M}{k \cdot H \sqrt{N'}}} \, (H - X) \, \frac{2}{z + 1} \tag{13}$$

or most generally:

$$d = \Pi \, \frac{1}{N'^{\frac{w}{2}}} \sqrt{\frac{M}{k \cdot H \cdot N'^{w}}} \, (H - X) \, \frac{2}{z + 1} \tag{14}$$

where k, Π, and w are also constant values for the species. Therefore:

$$c = \frac{\Pi}{\sqrt{k}} = \text{constant for the species} \tag{15}$$

It is not difficult to find out that the term $(k \cdot H \cdot N'^{w})$ expresses the volume of wood per surface unit which it is maximally possible to obtain in the conditions determined by the factors k, H, and N':

$$M_{max} = k \cdot H \cdot N'^{w} \tag{16}$$

Now for the answer to the question: What volume may be maximally enclosed on the surface equal to H^2, therefore in the cube equal to H^3? Expressing this maximum volume by the symbol m, the maximal volume may be calculated when $z = 1$ and when $\dfrac{M}{k \cdot H \cdot N'^{w}} = 1$; thus:

$$\frac{m}{H^3} = \frac{\pi}{4} \cdot \frac{d^2 \cdot H \cdot F \cdot N'}{H^3} = \frac{\dfrac{\pi}{4} \left[\dfrac{\Pi}{N'^{\frac{w}{2}}} (H - X) \right]^2 H \cdot F \cdot N'}{H^3}$$

$$= \frac{\pi}{4} \cdot \frac{\Pi^2}{N'^{w}} \cdot \left[\left(\frac{H - X}{H} \right)^2 \cdot F \right] N' = \frac{\pi \cdot \Pi^2}{4} \left[\left(\frac{H - X}{H} \right)^2 F \right] N'^{(1 - w)}$$

where π = 3.1416, F = form factor (for normal crowding and "compactness"

conditions).

Now:

$$\left(\frac{H - X}{H}\right)^2 \cdot F = \theta = \text{constant for the species} \qquad (1$$

Expression (17) is right from the practical point of view.

So:

$$\frac{m}{H^3} = \frac{\pi}{4} \Pi^2 \cdot \theta \cdot \overset{\prime}{N}(1 - w)$$

as:

$$\frac{M}{m} = \frac{P}{H^2}$$

therefore:

$$M = m \frac{P}{H^2}$$

thus:

$$M_{max} = \frac{\pi}{4} \Pi^2 \cdot \theta \frac{P}{H^2} H^3 \cdot \overset{\prime}{N}(1 - w)$$

and when

$$w = 1 - w$$

$$M_{max} = \left[\frac{\pi}{4} \Pi^2 \theta \quad P\right] H \cdot \overset{\prime}{N}{}^w \qquad ($$

where:

$$\frac{\pi}{4} \Pi^2 \cdot \theta \cdot P = k$$

Note again that when X = 1.3 meters and when 10 meters < H < 40 meters

then in practice:

$$\theta = \text{constant for the species}$$

So the maximum value:

$$M_{max} = k \cdot H \cdot N'^w \tag{16}$$

where:

$$w \approx 0.5$$

and is to be determined more precisely.

Thus:

$$M_{max} \approx k \cdot H \cdot \sqrt{N'} \tag{16a}$$

The expression $\dfrac{M}{M_{max}}$ may be represented by the symbol x.

$$\frac{M}{M_{max}} = \frac{M}{k \cdot H \cdot N'^w} = x \tag{19}$$

Then we may name the term x "compactness factor," which of course has the property

$$0 \leq x \leq 1$$

It is noteworthy that because

$$\Pi \approx \alpha \sqrt[4]{N'} \tag{11}$$

then precisely in one locality:

$$M_{max} = k_I \cdot H \cdot N'$$

where k_I is a coefficient which is constant in one locality.

The camouflage of the separate influence of the compactness factor and simultaneously of the separate influence of the site indicator in formula (10) is a result of the fusion of these parameters into the term:

$$\frac{M}{H \cdot N'}$$

So there it was exceedingly difficult to consider what the function M_{max} = $f(\overset{\prime}{N})$ is. Just the detection that $\Pi = f_1(\overset{\prime}{N})$ expresses approximately a fourth root of the site indicator enables the taking of steps to explain the details of constructions of the formulas describing the d and M_{max}.

These considerations enable the expression of the following principle: The maximum attainable volume of wood per surface unit in a pure, even-aged stand is directly proportional to the mean stand height and approximately directly proportional to the square root of the site indicator (formula 16a).

Thus the stand intensity:

$$\frac{M_{max}}{H} = k \cdot \overset{\prime}{N}^w$$

in conditions determined by the parameter k in one productive capacity of locality, is a constant value regardless of age; this observation was made by the Polish scientist K. Suchecki (1947). And here is obtained a relationship between the stand intensity and the site indicator.

This result allows expression of a second principle, namely: The maximum stand intensity is a constant value in one productive capacity of locality; therefore it is a value which is independent of the age of the stand. This principle the author calls the principle of ecological saturation of a forest stand.

Using formula (14) the numerical value of k may be determined. When:

$$M = M_{max}$$

and

$$z = 1$$

and

$$x = 1$$

then

$$\mathrm{d} = d_1$$

In other words, d_1 means average stand diameter b.h. when crowding and compactness factors are equal to 1.

Thus

$$d_1 = \frac{\prod}{N^{\frac{w}{2}}} (H - X) \tag{12b}$$

After substitution and reduction:

$$M_{max} = \frac{\pi}{4} \prod^2 \cdot \theta \, P \cdot H \cdot N^w \tag{18}$$

(when $w = 0.5$)

In the formula:

$$d = c \sqrt{\frac{M}{H \cdot N} (H - X) \frac{2}{z + 1}} \tag{12a}$$

the coefficient c is constant for a definite species. This is an important circumstance from the practical point of view. This formula enables prediction of the value of diameter without the necessity of knowing the value of $\prod$, or k, or w. But it is quite a different matter in the case of the determination of the maximum possible volume.

In formula (18) the parameter $\prod$ is in the second power in comparison with the same parameter represented in the first power in the formula determining d (formula 13). Consequently, it is quite impossible to use a mean value of $\prod$ in formula (18), when $\prod$ is determined by approximation in order to predict the value of diameter.

For Scots pine stands the numerical values represent on the average:

$$c = \frac{\Pi}{\sqrt{k}} = 0.0166$$

$$\Pi = 0.0309$$

with the confidence coefficient $\beta = 0.70$ and by the standard deviation $\xi_1 = 5$ per cent. This means that when the formula is utilized determining the value of d and when the value $c = 0.0166$ and the present-day value of z are used, then in 70 cases out of 100 the formula gives a result having an error between the limits of $- 5$ to $+ 5$ per cent. On the average this formula works with a coefficient of variation ± 4.85 per cent when only the present value of z is known.

Therefore, if the requirements for the confidence (in relation to the volume) are increased to 0.99, then:

$$\xi_2 = s \cdot t_\beta$$

and when:

$$k_1 = (n - 1) = 269$$
$$t_{0.99} = 2.576$$
$$\xi_2 = 4.85\% \cdot 2.576 = 13.7\%$$

So if this value is added to the mean value of Π, an approximately maximal value with the confidence coefficient of 0.99 is obtained, namely:

$$\Pi_{smax} = 0.0309 + 0.0042 = 0.0351$$

The value calculated in the above-mentioned way may be named "submaximal value" and may be expressed by the symbol Π_{smax}. Using this value for calculating the submaximal value of the volume, one may expect that, in 99 cases out of 100, for stands diagnosed as fully stocked one

will not meet a stand that would have a volume greater than calculated
by means of formula (18) or (16). But even if it should happen, the
difference between the calculated value and the experimental one would
be quite small.

Finally, it should be added that the experimental material used
to define these values relates to an assemblage of stands that have been
diagnosed by skilled foresters as fully stocked. Formulas (16) and (18)
will be proper for the determination of the compactness factor. This
procedure will be more rational than one based on values from yield
tables now available.

In this treatment of maximal volume the actual volume of stands
which have been diagnosed as sufficiently fully stocked, divided by the
submaximal value, equals about 0.8. It is worth noting that foresters
believe, merely on the basis of many ocular observations, that the
stocking of most of the stands classified as normally stocked (according
to yield tables) amounts to approximately 80 per cent of the value that
it would be possible to obtain.

It must be emphasized that the coefficient k may be treated as a
constant value only if stands which have attained a sufficiently great
height are compared:

$$M_{max} = \left[\frac{\pi}{4} \Pi^2 \, \theta \, P \right] \cdot H \cdot N^{'w} \qquad (18)$$

where

$$\frac{\pi}{4} \Pi^2 \cdot \theta \cdot P = k$$

and

$$\theta = \left(\frac{H - X}{H} \right)^2 \cdot F$$

Then if the value of F is treated as practically constant (as for instance during a thinning period):

$$M_{max} = k \cdot \left(\frac{H - X}{H}\right)^2 H \cdot N^{'W} = k \cdot \sqrt{N'} \; \frac{(H - X)^2}{H} \qquad ($$

where

$$k = \frac{\pi}{4} \prod{}^2 \cdot P \cdot F \qquad ($$

Thus to compare stands of various heights it is proper to use formula (16b).

Chapter V

DETERMINATION OF VALUES OF COEFFICIENTS

The basic formula:

$$d = c \sqrt{\frac{M}{N' \cdot H}} \; (H - X) \; \frac{2}{z + 1} \tag{12a}$$

is inconvenient if there is no graph nor alinement chart to determine the value of N' as a function of age and height. And this situation exists for most species.

As it is known that

$$z + 1 \approx 2 \sqrt{z}, \; or, \; \frac{1}{\sqrt{z}} \approx \frac{2}{z + 1}$$

if the value of z is not too much different from 1.0, the formula may be transformed as follows:

$$d = c \sqrt{\frac{M}{N' \cdot H}} \; \frac{1}{\sqrt{z}} \; (H - X)$$

But as:

$$z = \frac{N_r}{N} = \frac{N_r}{N' \dfrac{P}{H^2}} = \frac{N_r \cdot H^2}{N' \cdot P}$$

thus:

$$d = c \sqrt{P} \sqrt{\frac{M_r}{H \cdot N_r}} \left(1 - \frac{X}{H} \right) \tag{22a}$$

where:

M = M_r = actual volume per surface unit.

Now:

$$c \sqrt{P} = \varsigma$$

In the inches-and-feet system of measurement customary in the United
States:

$$d = \varsigma \sqrt{\frac{M_r}{H \cdot N_r}} \left(1 - \frac{4.5}{H}\right)$$

Since one may obtain values of d, M_r, H, and N_r from observations, the
value of ς can be calculated, and after this the value of c may be computed, using formula (21).

From the practical point of view formula (22) is useful, because
using it one does not need to know the age of stand; thus results of
calculation are free from inaccuracies of determination of the value N.
Furthermore, the influence of errors in measuring tree height on the
accuracy of the value H is considerably less than in the basic formula
(12a).

If a large amount of mensurational data is available, a nearly
true value for the coefficient c can be obtained.

In Table 10 are observations from 70 experimental loblolly pine
(Pinus taeda L.) plots in central Louisiana, presented in a progress report, "Thinning in a Loblolly Spacing Plantation," dated May 6, 1953, by
W. F. Mann, Jr., Southern Forest Experiment Station, Alexandria, Louisiana. Using this material the author computed that ς = 24.7, if the volume M_r is given in merchantable cubic feet of peeled wood to a 3.0-inch
top inside bark, if H is the average height of dominant and codominant
trees (100 largest trees) per acre, designated by $H_{(!)}$, and if N_r is the

TABLE 10.   Excerpts of the calculation of the value of Ç in formula (22) for 70 loblolly pine plantation plots near Alexandria, Louisiana. Basic data obtained from W. F. Mann, Jr., Alexandria Research Center, Southern Forest Experiment Station. Measurements made in 1953 at age 25, five years after thinning.

Plot #	Initial spacing, feet	No. trees per acre N_r	Total vol., cu. ft. i.b.[*] M_r	Av. ht. dominants $H_{(!)}$	Av. d.b.h. exp. d_r	calc.[**] d_f	Ç calc.
3	4x4	310	1370	48.0	6.3	6.4	22.9
6	4x4	410	1800	48.5	6.3	6.3	23.1
2	4x4	550	2560	47.5	6.4	6.6	22.6
5	4x4	520	1780	46.5	5.8	5.7	23.7
1	4x4	610	2050	50.0	5.8	5.5	24.6
4	4x4	510	2080	49.5	6.2	6.1	23.8
5	6x6	330	1720	54.0	6.8	6.6	23.9
10	6x6	340	1670	50.0	6.6	6.6	23.2
15	6x6	200	1630	60.0	8.2	7.9	24.1
20	6x6	240	1670	56.0	7.6	7.5	23.5
1	6x6	280	2300	55.5	8.1	8.2	22.9
4	6x6	420	1860	47.0	6.3	6.4	22.7
6	6x6	470	2250	51.0	6.5	6.5	23.3
9	6x6	350	3170	57.5	8.6	8.5	23.5
11	6x6	430	2130	48.0	6.6	6.8	22.7
14	6x6	390	1740	53.0	6.3	6.2	23.7
16	6x6	300	1960	58.0	7.4	7.2	23.9
19	6x6	310	1590	54.5	6.7	6.5	23.8
2P	10x10	370	3680	57.0	8.9	9.0	23.1
2	10x10	220	2510	56.5	9.5	9.7	23.0
7	10x10	340	3130	55.0	8.6	8.8	22.9
12	10x10	270	2900	58.0	9.3	9.3	23.5
17	10x10	330	3140	57.0	8.8	8.8	23.4
1P	10x10	140	2670	62.0	12.0	12.2	23.3
1	10x10	240	2560	58.5	9.2	9.2	23.4
6	10x10	350	3170	55.0	8.6	8.7	23.1
11	10x10	260	3060	56.5	9.7	9.8	23.1
						Total	1626.5

$$\text{Av. } Ç = \frac{1626.5}{70} = 23.2$$

[*]   computed by converting merchantable volume to total volume by use of factors varying with average d.b.h.

[**]   calculated from formula (22) by use of mean Ç = 23.2

number of trees above 3.6 inches in diameter breast high. If M_r in formula (22) is given in cubic feet of peeled wood for the entire stem, ς =
23.2.

In Table 11, as an illustration, the author presents the most
extreme values of M_r, N_r, and H.

If the volume M_r represents the volume of unpeeled trees, and N_r
represents all trees in the stand, then ς = 21.0.

Formula (22) was tested against basic data supplied by Professor
B. A. Bateman, School of Forestry, Louisiana State University. Table 12
shows the data and the computed values of the average stand diameters.
The data describe natural loblolly pine stands located near Hammond,
Louisiana. Because the volume data represent unpeeled trees, a value of
21.0 was used for ς in the formula. The standard deviation of calculated diameters in relation to experimental diameters in Table 12 is only
one per cent. It may be estimated that the accuracy of determination of
the average diameter is about $\pm$ 1 per cent (if diameter is about 10 inches), and at the same time, the accuracy of calculated values is at
least $\pm$ 0.5 per cent (as the values are rounded to the second place
after the decimal point). Thus the deviation of about $\pm$ 1.5 per cent
may be treated as an understandable accuracy limit for single observations when diameter is about 10 inches.

These examples could be multiplied endlessly.

Formula (22) may be used to predict the average stand diameter,
since the value of N depends on the degree of intensity of thinning; the
future height is easy to predict by means of a graph of height as a
function of the age and site class; and the volume is also predictable

TABLE 11. Excerpt from Table 10, showing most extreme values* for loblolly pine plots near Alexandria, Louisiana.

Plot #	Initial spacing, feet	No. trees per acre N_r	Total vol., cu. ft. i.b. M_r	Av. ht. dominants $H_{(!)}$	Av. d.b.h. exp. d_r	calc. d_f
3	4x4	310	*1370	48.0	6.3	6.4
9	8x8	460	*3770	55.5	8.1	8.2
1	4x4	*610	2050	50.0	5.8	5.5
5P	10x10	*130	2300	63.5	11.6	11.4
5	4x4	520	1780	*46.5	5.8	5.7
3	10x10	180	3050	*63.5	11.4	11.1

TABLE 12. Test of formula (22) for data from loblolly pine plots near
Hammond, Louisiana. Age 33 years, 5 years after thinning. Data supplied by Professor B. A. Bateman, Louisiana State University.

Plot #	No. trees per acre N_r (all trees)	Merch. vol. cu. ft. M_r (including bark)	$H_{(!)}$	Av. d.b.h., inches exp. d_r	calc. d_f
11	231	4777	88	9.9	10.1
8	195	4608	88	10.4	10.5
12	166	4257	88	10.8	10.9
7	160	4257	88	11.3	11.2
4	136	3987	88	11.6	11.8
13	115	3726	88	12.1	12.1
14	100	2465	88	12.5	12.5

by use of E. Genrhardt's formula, which will be a subject of considera-

tion in one of the subsequent chapters.

Although the last formula is a sufficient tool for practical

purposes, also to be coped with are some other magnitudes which repre-

sent certain essential characteristics of a forest stand.

It is of great interest to know the values of N as a function of

age and height. If much experimental data are available, one may choose

from them some series of stands of the same productive capacity of site,
but of different crowding. Thus may be calculated the values of $\overset{\shortmid}{N}$ using
the basic formula:

$$d = c \sqrt{\frac{M}{H \cdot \overset{\shortmid}{N}}} \cdot H \cdot \frac{2}{z + 1} - \Delta = c \sqrt{\frac{M \, H}{\overset{\shortmid}{N}}} \cdot \frac{2}{\frac{N \cdot H^2}{\overset{\shortmid}{N} \cdot P} + 1} - \Delta$$

When it is known from an experiment the values of d, M, H, and $c = \dfrac{\varsigma}{\sqrt{P}}$,

by the use of substitutions and gradual approximations, one can get at
the values of $\overset{\shortmid}{N}$ for each site class.

Of course this work is time-consuming; the more so as this method requires a special smoothing calculation because each observation
contains some errors of measurement.

It would be meaningless to give here these simple but very laborious operations; instead, it will suffice to say that, using material
from the Southern Forest Experiment Station supplied by W. F. Mann, Jr.,
Alexandria, Louisiana, the author was able to determine the values of $\overset{\shortmid}{N}$
for some site classes and afterward was able to find that for loblolly
pine in the measurement system customary in the United States:

$$H_{(\text{\tiny !})} = 1.64 \, \overset{\shortmid}{N} \left\{ \ln \left(1 + \frac{a}{A} \right) - 0.386 \right\}$$

For the time being it is not known exactly what the values of A
are for the various site classes. To develop accurate values of A for
the last equation investigation must be made of the age of culmination
of height growth in connection with the productive capacity of locality;
but as height growth is greatly affected by weather conditions during
the year in which the growth was accomplished (or maybe also during

several years before the accomplishing of the growth), the effect of meteorological elements on this growth must be studied. Because my work in Louisiana was limited by time, I was unable to investigate this problem. Therefore, values of A used are only first approximations, determined by trial-and-error processes with the use of data for loblolly pine in Louisiana provided by W. F. Mann, Jr. Figure 9 shows the approximate relationship of A to $\overset{\scriptscriptstyle\prime}{N}$. Then Figure 10 was prepared, which enables determination of the value of $\overset{\scriptscriptstyle\prime}{N}$, given the stand age and height.

The graph of Figure 10 is also only provisional but may be used for many practical purposes and scientific investigations.

As an illustration how formula (12a) and the graph in Figure 10 work, two tables (Tables 13 and 14) are presented. To facilitate the calculation, the author transformed formula (12a) as follows:

$$d = c \sqrt{\frac{M}{H \cdot \overset{\scriptscriptstyle\prime}{N}}} \ (H - X) \ \frac{2}{z + 1} \tag{12a}$$

$$d = (2c) \sqrt{\frac{M \ H}{\overset{\scriptscriptstyle\prime}{N}}} \cdot \frac{1}{z + 1} - \Delta \tag{12c}$$

The value of ς equal to 24.7 has already been determined, and it is already known how to compute the value of c from formula (21):

$$\varsigma = c \sqrt{P}$$

$$c = \frac{\varsigma}{\sqrt{P}}$$

$$c = \frac{24.7}{\sqrt{43560}} \tag{21}$$

$$c = \frac{24.7}{208.7} = 0.118$$

Thus in particular numbers for loblolly pine:

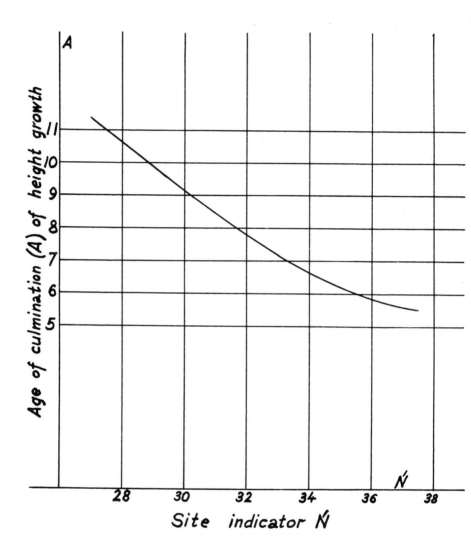

FIGURE 9. Provisional graph of the relationship between site indicator (Ṅ) and age of height-growth culmination (A) for loblolly pine (<u>Pinus taeda</u> L.) stands in Louisiana.

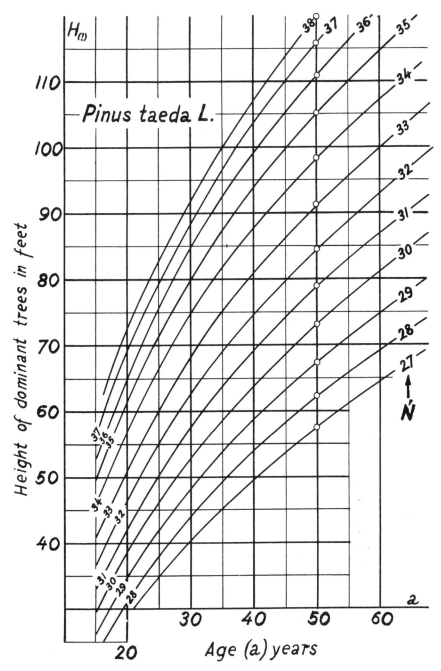

FIGURE 10. Stand height as a function of age a and site indicator Ń for loblolly pine (Pinus taeda L.) stands in Louisiana [see equation (7b)].

TABLE 13. Test of formula (12d) for computing average stand diameter
for loblolly pine plantation plots near Alexandria, Louisiana. Basic
data given in Table 10.

Plot #	Initial spacing, feet	Site indicator N	Crowding factor z	d.b.h., inches exp. d_r	d.b.h., inches calc. d_f
3	4x4	30.4	0.54	6.3	6.0
6	4x4	30.4	0.73	6.3	6.2
2	4x4	30.3	0.94	6.4	6.5
5	4x4	30.1	0.86	5.8	5.5
1	4x4	31.0	1.13	5.8	5.3
4	4x4	30.9	0.93	6.2	6.0
5	6x6	31.8	0.70	6.8	6.4
10	6x6	31.0	0.63	6.6	6.4
15	6x6	32.9	0.503	8.2	7.5
20	6x6	32.2	0.54	7.6	7.2
1	6x6	32.2	0.61	8.1	8.1
4	6x6	30.2	0.71	6.3	6.3
6	6x6	31.2	0.90	6.5	6.4
9	6x6	32.5	0.82	8.6	8.6
11	6x6	30.4	0.75	6.6	6.7
14	6x6	31.6	0.80	6.3	6.0
16	6x6	32.6	0.71	7.4	7.4
19	6x6	31.9	0.66	6.7	6.3
3	6x6	32.2	0.83	8.2	8.2
8	6x6	33.2	0.70	7.9	7.5
13	6x6	30.1	0.70	7.1	7.2
18	6x6	33.2	0.76	7.6	7.2
2	6x6	31.4	1.13	7.0	7.0
7	6x6	31.3	1.13	6.6	6.6
17	6x6	31.4	0.83	7.9	8.2
12	6x6	32.9	1.48	6.7	5.9
4P	8x8	33.0	0.53	9.3	8.8
4	8x8	32.0	0.39	8.6	8.0
8	8x8	32.2	0.55	7.8	7.5
12	8x8	31.0	0.39	8.1	7.8
16	8x8	31.8	0.50	8.7	8.7
3P	8x8	31.5	0.68	8.5	8.9
3	8x8	32.0	0.58	7.8	7.6
7	8x8	31.8	0.59	8.0	8.0
11	8x8	31.7	0.62	8.0	8.0
15	8x8	32.3	0.79	7.9	7.9
2P	8x8	32.2	0.83	8.3	8.4
10	8x8	31.8	0.74	7.8	7.8
14	8x8	31.9	0.64	9.0	9.3
2	8x8	31.6	0.55	8.4	8.9
6	8x8	32.7	0.58	8.6	8.1

TABLE 13. (continued) Test of formula (12d) for computing average stand diameter for loblolly pine plantation plots near Alexandria, Louisiana. Basic data given in Table 10.

Plot #	Initial spacing, feet	Site indicator N	Crowding factor z	d.b.h., inches exp. d_r	d.b.h., inches calc. d_f
1P	8x8	31.4	1.01	7.4	7.6
1	8x8	32.2	0.815	7.6	7.7
5	8x8	31.6	0.94	7.6	7.7
9	8x8	32.2	1.01	8.1	8.4
13	8x8	32.9	1.18	7.8	7.8
5P	10x10	33.5	0.36	11.6	10.4
5	10x10	33.4	0.57	10.2	9.8
10	10x10	31.7	0.31	9.1	8.1
15	10x10	32.7	0.36	10.1	9.1
20	10x10	32.3	0.43	9.4	8.9
4P	10x10	31.9	0.66	9.1	9.3
4	10x10	33.0	0.51	10.0	9.5
9	10x10	32.0	0.54	9.1	9.1
14	10x10	32.6	0.50	9.7	9.4
19	10x10	32.4	0.41	9.5	8.9
3P	10x10	32.2	0.675	9.2	9.2
3	10x10	33.5	0.50	11.4	11.0
8	10x10	32.3	0.59	9.5	9.6
13	10x10	32.0	0.35	9.5	9.5
18	10x10	32.6	0.43	10.0	9.4
2P	10x10	32.4	0.85	8.9	9.1
2	10x10	32.3	0.50	9.5	9.3
7	10x10	32.0	0.74	8.6	8.8
12	10x10	32.6	0.64	9.3	9.3
17	10x10	32.4	0.76	8.8	8.8
1P	10x10	33.3	0.37	12.0	11.1
1	10x10	32.7	0.58	9.2	9.0
6	10x10	32.0	0.76	8.6	8.7
11	10x10	32.3	0.59	9.7	9.7

$$d = 0.236 \sqrt{\frac{M\,H}{N}} \cdot \frac{1}{z + 1} - 0.6 \qquad (12d)$$

If one uses values of N read from the graph (Figure 10), the basic formula (12d) may be tested, as well as the validity of values of N which have been defined above.

TABLE 14. Test of formula (12d) for computing average stand diameter for loblolly pine stands near Urania, Louisiana. Data supplied by W. F. Mann, Jr., Southern Forest Experiment Station. Measurements were made 5 to 6 years after thinning.

Year	Degree of thin- ning	Age	Ht. of dominant trees	No. of trees per acre	Site indi- cator	Vol. in merch. cu. ft.	Crowd- ing factor	d.b.h., in.	
								exp.	calc.
	a		$H_{(!)}$	N_r	N'	M_r	z	d_r	d_f
1925	heavy	32	62	312	31.4	2201	0.88	7.6	7.6
1925	light	32	60	470	31.0	2581	1.25	6.8	6.8
1925	unthinned	32	63	540	31.5	3180	1.56	6.8	6.7
1930	heavy	37	64	272	30.6	2389	0.86	8.2	8.3
1930	light	37	63	352	30.5	2682	1.05	7.7	7.9
1930	unthinned	37	65	432	30.8	3236	1.36	7.5	7.7
1935	heavy	42	67	252	30.3	2721	0.86	8.8	9.2
1935	light	42	67	276	30.3	2766	0.94	8.5	8.1
1935	unthinned	42	69	372	30.5	3480	1.33	8.0	8.4
1940	heavy	47	73	156	30.5	2513	0.61	10.1	10.7
1940	light	47	74	204	30.6	2870	0.84	9.5	10.1
1940	unthinned	47	77	320	31.1	3815	1.40	8.8	8.9
1946	heavy	53	81	144	30.9	3059	0.70	11.2	11.8
1946	light	53	79	192	30.5	3370	0.90	10.4	10.9
1946	unthinned	53	78	252	30.4	4018	1.16	9.9	10.5
1951	heavy	58	85	72	31.0	2156	0.38	13.1	12.5
1951	light	58	82	116	31.3	3022	0.57	12.3	12.2
1951	unthinned	58	88	216	31.4	4177	1.22	10.6	10.9

In Table 13 the standard deviation of formula values of diameter in relation to the experimental diameters is equal to $\pm$ 4.24 per cent, which is approximately the same as for Scots pine.

It is understandable that in a given stand the value of N' changes between certain limits, since height growth is a function of meteorological elements. When the number N' is treated as a stable value in a certain point of locality, the site must be considered as independent of vacillation of weather. Values so treated ought to be represented in yield tables. Now compare the tabular number with values obtained using formula (7b). Loblolly pine yield tables were prepared by W. H. Meyer (1942), based on stand records on 273 sample plots ranging in age from 19 to 77 years (50 per cent of the plots being in site class 85-94); the height values are presented in Table 15. Not shown are the values for site index 120 and for ages above 60 years, because they are based on very few observations.

It is remarkable that the deviations between the calculated values and tabular ones are evidently greater for the younger ages. This probably derives from two causes:

1. In the young age classes only a few plots are represented in the data.

2. The vagaries of weather as affecting total height are more important in the younger age classes than in the older. Of course, this influence is distinctly visible if all observations were made in only a short period of time, and this situation exists in the case of observations by Meyer.

Notwithstanding these circumstances, there is quite good agreement between calculated values and tabular ones. But any doubts may be resolved by comparison of calculated quantities with raw observations.

Compare such data using Table 16.

The standard deviation of calculated heights in relation to the experimental heights is below one per cent. Since the inaccuracy of measurement of height is known to be greater than $\pm$ 1 per cent, it must be concluded that the agreement of the theory with experimental data is excellent.

A very difficult task is the determination of the values of Π,

TABLE 15. Comparison of calculated values of height with heights as given in yield tables for even-aged stands of loblolly pine in northern Louisiana (Meyer, 1942). The symbol n means the number of experimental plots in each class. Formula (7b) was used to calculate heights.

Site index →	70			80			90			100			110		
N' →	29.5			31.0			33.0			34.5			35.7		
Age ↓	calc.	tab.	n	calc.	tab.	n	calc.	tab.	n	calc.	tab.	n	calc.	tab.	n
	Heights in feet of dominant and codominant trees														
20	36	35	1	42	40	5	51	45	5	57	50	4	64	-	0
30	50	52	1	58	59	5	68	66	8	75	74	9	84	81	2
40	61	-	0	70	71	9	81	81	26	88	90	24	98	99	1
50	70	-	0	79	80	15	91	90	33	100	100	16	110	110	2
60	78	75	1	87	86	13	100	97	33	109	108	16	119	118	2

TABLE 16. Comparison of calculated values of height with heights as measured experimentally in a loblolly pine stand in Louisiana. Experimental data from a progress report on Castor Creek plots, dated February 1, 1951, by W. F. Mann, Jr., Southern Forest Experiment Station. Plot U-13 (unthinned). Formula (7b) was used to calculate heights.

Year	Age a (years)	N'	A (years)	Height (feet) exp. H_e	calc. H_f
1920	26	33.4	7.0	64	64
1925	31	33.1	7.1	71	70
1930	36	33.5	6.9	80	79
1935	41	33.5	6.9	86	85
1940	46	33.6	6.8	92	92
1946	52	34.4	6.5	103	102
1951	57	34.3	6.5	107	107
	Mean	33.7	6.8		

k, and w in the equations:

$$c = \frac{\Pi}{\sqrt{k}}$$
(15)

and

$$M_{max} = k \cdot H \cdot N'^{w}$$
(16)

In equation (15) it is known how to determine the value c, since it was explained above. And the value of Π may be determined from the equation:

$$\Pi = \alpha \cdot N'^{\frac{w}{2}}$$
(11a)

if the value of w is known.

Determination of the value of w from equation (16) is possible, but the form of equation is inconvenient: the value k in this way is determinable only simultaneously with the determination of the value of w, but in this way may be obtained different pairs of values k and w, depending on the quite insignificant differences in the materials with which one deals.

Therefore to determine these coefficients there must be available numerous observations obtained from a large range of sites. Unfortunately, for loblolly pine the author did not have available this sort of observation.

As an illustration, some approximate values for the coefficients k, w, and Π for loblolly pine are developed herein. For example, consider plot U-14 on Castor Creek, Louisiana.[1] In 1946 the characteristics of the stand were as follows:

---

[1] Progress report, Castor Thinning Study, by W. F. Mann, Jr., So. For. Exp. Station, Feb. 1, 1951.

age   a   = 52 years

height (dom.) $H_{(!)}$ = 109 feet

site indicator $\overset{,}{N}$ = 35.4

volume   M   = 7857 cubic feet
                              per acre (mer-
                              chantable)

diameter   d   = 15.1 inches

crowding factor z   = 1.3

From the equation:

$$d = \alpha H \frac{2}{z + 1} - \Delta$$

is obtained:

$$\alpha = \frac{(d + \Delta)(z + 1)}{2 H} \, .$$

For the above plot:

$$\alpha = \frac{(15.1 + 0.6)(1.3 + 1.0)}{2 \times 109} = 0.166$$

The existing volume on this plot is treated as maximally obtain-able, as this volume is extremely great. From equation (16)

$$k = \frac{M}{\overset{,}{N}{}^{w} \cdot H}$$

then:

$$\prod = c \sqrt{k}$$

or:

$$\prod = c \sqrt{\frac{M}{\overset{,}{N}{}^{w} \cdot H}}$$

Thus:

$$\alpha \overset{,}{N}{}^{\frac{w}{2}} = c \sqrt{\frac{M}{\overset{,}{N}{}^{w} \cdot H}}$$

or:

$$N^{'\frac{w}{2}} \cdot N^{'\frac{w}{2}} = \frac{c}{\alpha} \sqrt{\frac{M}{H}}$$

or:

$$N^{'w} = \frac{c}{\alpha} \sqrt{\frac{M}{H}}$$

therefore:

$$w = \frac{\log \dfrac{c}{\alpha} \sqrt{\dfrac{M}{H}}}{\log N^{'}}$$

To express the volume in total cubic feet the author has used a converting factor based on Tables 1 and 2 of U.S.D.A. Misc. Pub. 50 (U.S. Forest Service, 1929).

$$w = \frac{\log \left[\dfrac{0.118}{0.166} \sqrt{\dfrac{8250}{109}} \right]}{\log 35.4} = \frac{0.7913}{1.5490} = 0.51$$

It is worthwhile to emphasize that for Scots pine stands the most probable value for w is about 0.5. Then taking under consideration that all the above data are affected by errors of observations, one may use for approximate calculation a rounded value, w = 0.5. Thus the approximate value of k can now be calculated from formula (16b):

$$k = \frac{M_{max} \cdot H}{(H - 4.5)^2 \cdot N^{'w}} \gtrsim \frac{8250 \cdot 109}{10920 \cdot \sqrt{35.4}} = 13.8$$

Finally, the approximate submaximal value of Π may be determined from formula (15):

$$\Pi = c \sqrt{k} \gtrsim 0.4$$

Thus, the theory opens large prospects of research in the potential productive capacity of locality. No doubt further extensive research in this field is necessary.

Finally a return must be made to formula (22). This formula in fact expresses a very simple and quite understandable equation and contains only one innovation, namely the term between brackets, but the validity of the formula, which is a result of a transformation of the basic formula (12a), supports the argument that the basic formula is valid.

Every scientific investigation aiming at making generalizations and inquiring into the correlation among various characteristics is conducted by measurement. Thus, appropriate indices or characteristics that will aid in the comparison of given magnitudes need to be devised. From the many possible indices there ought to be employed in a scientific research only those that induce the least complications in the structure of equations.

The progress of separate disciplines of science depends on the introduction and application of certain notions that are pertinent to the definite discipline. These notions permit understanding of the phenomena; they enable the finding of a certain regularity in the course of the phenomena. Without development of these notions the progress of science is quite impossible. Thus these ideas, which have to be applicable in the definite branches of science, may not be shaped only from the point of view of a timber speculator. For instance, the notion of "merchantable volume" does not lend itself to the description of the structure of a forest stand. No doubt the most suitable expression of one of the characteristics of a forest stand is the total volume, i.e. volume of trunks and branches (including bark), without regard to their sizes. The transformation of total volume to merchantable volume is a separate question. But for a study of structure and dynamics of forest

stands total volume should be used. Unfortunately, the author did not

have at his disposal basic data expressed in total volume and, there-

fore, was obliged to use "merchantable volume." It is understandable

that the use of this timber-market notion involves some complications:

the younger the plantations, the lower the ratio of merchantable volume

to total volume.

It is not difficult to determine the other sources of the small

but still existing deviations of formula values from experimental val-

ues. Inaccuracies in the measurement of height and volume seem to be

the most serious cause, but also a certain error in the value of $\overset{\scriptscriptstyle |}{N}$,

which affects the calculation of normal crowding, does exist. Further-

more, the value of actual number of trees per surface unit is not free

from error, because the number of trees, being a function of magnitude

of area (P) and of crowding (z), depends on the size of plot, and the

error is especially noticeable when one deals with small plots and very

low crowding.

Efforts to express ecological relationships by mathematical

equations arise only from a desire to express them in an exact way.

The postulate of exactness makes the problem similar to problems met in

physics. Classical physics remains, as it has been, a prototype of an

exact science of nature.

Physics has confirmed the truth of a general principle, the

so-called principle of causality, which states that a definite cause

produces a definite outcome. This principle is based on conquests of

so-called classical physics, i.e. of that part of physics which is interested in bodies of the macroscopic world.

This principle may be stated as follows:

If a state of a certain system is definite (i.e. known) at a certain moment, consequently, preceding as well as subsequent states of this system are definite.

Thus it is evident that application of the principle of causality to a system of which the state is impossible to define would be without any sense. Therefore, this principle is not applicable in the "microcosmos." The calculation of probability is applicable to these elementary units, the collection of which creates a mass.

For instance, causality of a spontaneous change of some radioactive atom in the nearest unit of time is identical for all atoms of the same chemical element at every optional moment, i.e. it is neither possible to predict whether a certain definitely singled-out atom will be changed at a definite time nor what will be its behavior in general during a definite period. But with a collection of atoms, it is known without any doubt which quantity of atoms in the collection undergoes a definite change in a definite time unit.

Since in the macroscopic world we are coping with a tremendous number of atoms, probability -- treating the subject practically -- becomes certitude.

Although in elementary processes the calculation of probability is applicable, multitudinous processes are exactly determined, and these processes give signs of laws which are called "laws of nature."

Many times attention has been called to the fact that the same laws of probability are in force toward a member of human society, or a molecule of gas, or an atom of radioactive substance.

What is said here about probability and principle of causality has an analogous applicability toward trees and collections of them.

Toward elementary parts of forest collections -- toward trees, of course -- calculation of probability is applicable. We are unable to predict the destiny of each chosen tree just because we are unable to define the system (in the physical sense of the word) which consists of the tree with its neighbors together with the whole environment. Instead, if we consider a forest stand, we ought to know how to predict what quantity of trees in a forest stand in defined conditions will suffer defined change. A great quantity of elementary parts of a collection will cause probability to change into certainty. Great quantities of trees in a forest stand permit the process of reduction in number of trees per surface unit with increase in age to have just the development that is proper to phenomena which are considered in classical physics. The great quantity of trees in a forest stand suggests the idea that average diameter is a phenomenon which is expressible in the same way as phenomena which are the subject of classical physics.

It is known that differentiation is not only a symptom of life but is in general a symptom of nature. Also it cannot be forgotten that separate categories of objects differ from each other with a certain degree of differentiation. This degree of differentiation among individuals (examples of plants, animals, in the sphere of any population) is significant; nevertheless, in the case of large samples of homogeneous substances the degree of differentiation is comparatively tiny.

If, for degree of differentiation, is meant a deviation from an average value, then the standard deviation in the case of diameters of trees in an even-aged forest stand generally amounts to at least $\pm$ 25 to $\pm$ 35 per cent in relation to the average diameter. In simple words, this means that in even-aged forest stands the ratio of the diameter of the thinnest tree to the diameter of the thickest one is equal at least to approximately 1:3.

However the standard deviation of average diameter in a collection of stands which have identical height, volume, and number of trees per surface unit amounts to less than $\pm$ 5 per cent. This phenomenon is evident when formula (12a) is used, which gives results accompanied by very tiny errors.

Thus it is ascertained plainly that a forest stand is a "multitudinous phenomenon" in contrast to single trees -- "elementary creatures," and it is for this cause that forest stands are creations, the states of which can be exactly determined and expressed mathematically.

Chapter VI

FURTHER DISCUSSION ABOUT THE HYPOTHESIS

Foresters, especially those active in research work, have been searching for a long time for an objective measure of density. There is voluminous literature on the subject, but development of such a measure is proceeding slowly. Furthermore, the terminology used in many papers concerning the subject seems a veritable "Tower of Babel."

Intending to avoid any misunderstanding, the author has decided to use two notions, namely:

$$z = \text{crowding factor} = \frac{N_r}{N} = \frac{\text{actual number of trees per surface unit}}{\text{normal number of trees per surface unit}}$$

where "normal number" is defined by the hypothesis;

$$x = \text{compactness factor} = \frac{M_r}{M_{smax}} = \frac{\text{actual volume per surface unit}}{\text{submaximal volume per surface unit}}$$

where "submaximal volume" is defined by the above equations given in Chapter IV. The relation between these two factors is as follows:

$$x = z \ \frac{N \ \dfrac{d_r^2}{4} \ \pi \cdot F_r \cdot H_r}{M_{smax}}$$

where the terms with the subscript "r" mean the actual values, and without this mark, normal.

At this point consideration will be given the most extensive proposals of the measurement of factors related to the above-mentioned notions.

L. H. Reinecke (1933) presented a formula:

$$\log N = K - 1.6 \log d$$

where K is a constant.

Thus:

$$N \cdot d^{1.6} = j^K$$

As the number j is a logarithmic base, the term j^K is merely an index concerning a certain degree of utilization of space by trees in a forest stand. What is this measure? As is known:

$$d = c \sqrt{P} \; \sqrt{\frac{M}{H \cdot N} \left(1 - \frac{X}{H}\right)} \tag{2}$$

or

$$d^2 = C_*^2 \; \frac{M}{H} \; \frac{1}{N} \left(1 - \frac{X}{H}\right)^2$$

thus

$$N d^2 = \left[C_*^2 \left(1 - \frac{X}{H}\right)^2\right] \frac{M}{H}$$

where $\frac{M}{H}$ is called "stand intensity" (used for example by P. A. Briegleb, 1952), and the term between brackets may be treated as a constant value i (since $C_* = $ constant and the term $\left(1 - \frac{X}{H}\right)$ is nearly constant when values of H are not too small). Thus Reinecke's (j^K) is nothing else than:

$$j^K = \frac{M}{H} \cdot \frac{1}{d^{\,0.4}} \; i$$

Therefore this index, as well as the index K, is strongly related to stand intensity.

The author obtained similar results considering the proposal of S. R. Gevorkiantz (1937), who pointed out that the spacing of an even-aged stand can be measured by an index which is essentially an expression of the slenderness of the trees of which the stand is com-

posed. This equation in the simplest form is:

$$C = \frac{H}{d}$$

This means, of course, that in fully stocked stands of a given species

the ratio of height to diameter (slenderness) is a constant. He was

quite right.

It is known that:

$$d = \varsigma \sqrt{\frac{M}{H \cdot \overset{\prime}{N}} \ H \ \frac{2}{z + 1}} - \Delta \tag{22b}$$

Dividing by H:

$$\frac{d}{H} = \varsigma \sqrt{\frac{M}{H \cdot \overset{\prime}{N}}} \ \frac{2}{z + 1} - \frac{\Delta}{H}$$

the term $\frac{\Delta}{H}$ may be neglected, as it is very small.

$$\frac{d}{H} = \varsigma \sqrt{\frac{k \cdot H \cdot \overset{\prime}{N}^{w}}{H \cdot \overset{\prime}{N}}} \ \frac{2}{z + 1} = \varsigma \sqrt{k \ \frac{1}{\overset{\prime}{N}^{1-w}}} \ \frac{2}{z + 1}$$

Thus:

$$\frac{H}{d} = \frac{1}{2\varsigma} \sqrt{\frac{\overset{\prime}{N}^{1-w}}{k}} \ (z + 1)$$

Thus the ratio of height to diameter yields a value that is in fact pro-

portional to the crowding factor z.

It seems unnecessary to emphasize that the crowding factor z is

able to give great service, as it is represented in simple form in very

simple relationships, as follows:

$$d = \frac{\Pi}{\overset{\prime}{N}^{\frac{w}{2}}} \sqrt{x} \ (H - X) \ \frac{2}{z + 1} \tag{14b}$$

(where x is the compactness factor)

$$\frac{H - h}{H} = L^{\sqrt{z}}$$

where L = constant for a species. The last formula will be a subject

for consideration in a subsequent chapter.

Some of the most significant considerations concerning the mat-

ter of crowding criterion is found in the paper of F. C. Hummel (1954).

"How should the density of stocking be defined? In evenaged
uniform stands having a given mean diameter and mean height,
the density is proportional to the number of trees per hectare.
In stands with an equal number of trees per hectare and the
same mean diameter, density may be regarded as proportional to
height; and finally, in stands where the number of stems and
the mean heights are the same but the mean diameters differ,
the stand with the greater diameter gives the appearance of
being the denser."

The theory presented here satisfies completely these rational demands,

to wit:

1. Since

$$z = \frac{N_r}{N}$$

Hummel's first demand is completely satisfied, because the factor z is

not only proportional to the actual number of trees per surface unit but

is even directly proportional to this number.

2. Since

$$d = \frac{\Pi}{N^{\frac{w}{2}}} \sqrt{x} \ (H - X) \ \frac{2}{z + 1}$$

$$d = \frac{\Pi}{N^{\frac{w}{2}}} \sqrt{x} \cdot H \cdot \frac{2}{z + 1} - \Delta$$

$$z = \left(\frac{H}{d + \Delta}\right) \frac{2 \Pi}{N^{\frac{w}{2}}} \sqrt{x} - 1$$

Hummel's density and the crowding factor is in fact proportional to height if stands of the same diameters and the same numbers of trees per surface unit are considered. Thus Hummel's second demand is satisfied.

3. Finally, as

$$\frac{N_r}{N} = \left(\frac{H}{d + \Delta}\right) \frac{2 \prod}{N^{\frac{w}{2}}} \sqrt{x} - 1$$

in stands where the actual number of trees and heights are the same but the average diameters differ, the stand with the greater diameter shows that the stand is more compact, that the compactness factor (x) is greater. The third demand of Hummel is also completely satisfied, but in this case Hummel's statement about denseness applies exactly to compactness as used here.

Of course in a case when the heights and the compactness factors are the same, but the numbers of trees differ, the stand with the greater actual number of trees has the smaller diameter. This is understandable without explanation.

The compactness factor also plays in the above-mentioned relationships a very important role, but it was not treated in Hummel's paper, as he considered fully stocked stands.

In one of the preceding chapters consideration has been given some formulas concerning the normal number of trees per surface unit. In this chapter the subject must again be discussed, as other formulas of normal number are also sometimes applied.

In the United States some years ago the formula was generally used:

$$N = K \cdot D^n$$

(where D = average diameter b.h.), often in a logarithmic form:

$$\log N = n \cdot \log D + \log K$$

At the same time values of coefficients given by different authors differed seriously.

From the theory:

$$N = N' \frac{P}{H^2}$$

in stands normally crowded. Thus in stands fully stocked (compact), i.e. when z = 1 and x = 1 and when w = 0.5, from formula (14b):

$$d = \frac{\prod}{\sqrt[4]{N'}} \sqrt{x} \cdot H \cdot \frac{2}{(z+1)} - \Delta$$

then:

$$d = \frac{\prod}{\sqrt[4]{N'}} H - \Delta$$

or:

$$H = (d + \Delta) \frac{\sqrt[4]{N'}}{\prod}$$

thus:

$$N = N' \frac{P}{(d+\Delta)^2} \frac{\prod^2}{\sqrt{N'}}$$

or:

$$N = \left(\sqrt{N'} \cdot P \cdot \prod^2 \right) \cdot (d+\Delta)^{-2}$$

Hence the factor $K = \left(\sqrt{N'} \cdot P \cdot \prod^2 \right)$ depends on the productive capacity of the locality.

Particular values of coefficients are as follows:

Authors	n	K
Simmons and Schnur (1937)	-1.603	11890
McKinney et al. (1937)	-1.707	14415
Meyer (1942)	-1.906	19540

For the present study concerning loblolly pine stands in Louisiana, the following values for the coefficients were obtained:

Site index H_{50}	Site indicator N'	$D = (d + \Delta)$ $\Delta = 0.6$	K (provisionally, using $\prod = 0.40$)
70	29.5	-2.000	37800
80	31.0	-2.000	38800
90	33.0	-2.000	40100
100	34.5	-2.000	40900
110	35.7	-2.000	41600

These differences need an explanation. Since the coefficient K is directly proportional to the square root of the site indicator N', the influence of the productive capacity of the site is somewhat masked. Thus the magnitude of the coefficient depends on the particular site classes that are included in the experimental material with which one is dealing.

Furthermore, the equation of the form:

$$N = K \cdot D^n$$

has the property whereby many different pairs of values of K and n may be substituted, all of which will be satisfactory from the point of view of statistical conformity with the experimental data. This circumstance forces one to calculate the value of K, as well as n, independently of each other from other relationships where a surer calculation is available.

However, because the role of productive capacity of site is

perceptible, an experimental formula in which the role of an index of this capacity is expressed by basal area has been used recently in the United States. For instance D. W. Lynch (1958) used the formula:

$$N = \frac{G^{b_3}}{H^{b_1}} \cdot j^{b_0 + b_2 \frac{1}{a}}$$

where

j = base of logarithms

b_0 to b_3 = coefficients to be computed

a = age

G = basal area

For ponderosa pine stands Lynch computed:

$b_1 = 2.61$

$b_3 = 1.46$

$b_2 = -11.2$

Thus the last formula may be simplified and partially generalized with the equation:

$$N = \frac{G}{H^{1.79}} f(a)$$

The basal area can be expressed using the indicator $\overset{\shortmid}{N}$, since:

$$\text{basal area} = G = \frac{\pi}{4} d^2 \cdot N$$

and, as in normally crowded and fully compact stands:

$$d = \frac{\Pi}{\sqrt[4]{\overset{\shortmid}{N}}} (H - \mathcal{X})$$

and as is known:

$$N = \overset{\shortmid}{N} \frac{P}{H^2}$$

then:

$$G = \frac{\pi}{4} \frac{\Pi^2}{\sqrt{N'}} (H - X)^2 N \frac{P}{H^2}$$

thus:

$$G = \left[\frac{\pi}{4} \Pi^2 \cdot P\right] \sqrt{N'} \left(1 - \frac{X}{H}\right)^2 \qquad (23)$$

or more generally:

$$G = \left[\frac{\pi}{4} \Pi^2 \cdot P\right] N'^w \left(1 - \frac{X}{H}\right)^2 \qquad (23a)$$

but in one site class, or when stands do not seriously differ as to site

class:

$$G = \left[\frac{\pi}{4} \alpha^2 \cdot P\right] N' \left(1 - \frac{X}{H}\right)^2 \qquad (24)$$

therefore:

$$N = \frac{G}{H^2} \left[\frac{1}{\frac{\pi}{4} \cdot \alpha^2 \cdot P \cdot \left(1 - \frac{X}{H}\right)^2}\right] P \qquad (25)$$

where, of course, the term between brackets is f(a).

There is sufficient conformity between the theory presented here
and the structure of the experimental formula used by D. W. Lynch (1958).

But here also a very important restriction must be observed:
The last formula is applicable only to one site class. For different
site classes it is necessary to use another:

$$N = \frac{G^2}{H^2} \left[\frac{1}{\frac{\pi}{4} \Pi^2 \cdot \left(1 - \frac{X}{H}\right)^2}\right]^2 \frac{1}{P}$$

To express actual site quality the height of stand is commonly
used: in the continent of Europe, as a rule, the mean height of trees
of average diameter; in America, most commonly, the height of dominant

and codominant trees. Although the mean height of the tree of average
diameter is a precisely determined notion, its usefulness as an expression of site quality in fact is limited to stands that have normal
crowding and compactness. Similarly, the height of dominant and codominant trees is not an objective notion, although it may be made more objective, using the measurement of 100 of the thickest trees in a stand
(proposal of the Forestry Commission in England -- see P. Braathe,
1957). But this amendment may only be satisfactory if heavy thinnings
are not applied, as these operations may change the average height of
these 100 trees without changing the actual site quality.

Observations in Russia published by Eytingen (1949) indicate
that in the process of natural elimination of trees from a forest stand
(not influenced by human activity) only the trees die that have had a
diameter less than average in the stand. From the biological point of
view it also seems to be more valid to remove from the stand these trees
which are growing less, are genetically handicapped, and are giving way
in competition.

It is also possible to demonstrate mathematically, using known
relationships between separate forest stand characteristics, that only
by thinnings which remove trees of diameter less than average, may the
maximum final crop (measured in cubic volume units) be obtained.

Thus if the stands that are thinned from below are considered,
one may expect that the height of the 100 trees of largest diameter can
give the most objective expression of the productive capacity of the
locality. For this reason, in the above-given generalizations "the mean
height" may be stated as "the mean height of the 100 trees of largest

diameter in the stand." This height has been denoted here by $H_{(!)}$.

The most commonly used measure of site quality in the United States is so-called site index, i.e. the height reached by a forest stand at a given age. The concept was evolved in this country during and after World War I, chiefly by F. Roth, R. Watson, and E. H. Frothingham (cited from Spurr, 1952).

In comparison to the method used in Europe this concept is, without doubt, incomparably more rational, as the height of dominant trees at age a (H_a) is a true number. In contrast, in Europe the site-class designation is actually no number at all, but only a symbol, like a sign of the zodiac.

The site indicator ($\overset{\shortmid}{N}$) which the author introduced is proportional to this American site index, since:

$$H_{(a)} = C_* \overset{\shortmid}{N} \left\{ \ln\left(1 + \frac{a}{A}\right) - 0.386 \right\}$$

and, for instance when a = 50, for loblolly pine

$$H_{(50)} = 1.64\ \overset{\shortmid}{N} \left\{ \ln\left(1 + \frac{50}{A}\right) - 0.386 \right\}$$

But the site indicator $\overset{\shortmid}{N}$ which is used has a marked superiority in relation to other site indices, because the term $\overset{\shortmid}{N}$ is represented in the most important relationships among forest stand characteristics in comparatively simple form, namely:

$$\text{normal number of trees per surface unit} = N = \overset{\shortmid}{N}\ \frac{P}{H^2_{(!)}}$$

$$\text{crowding factor} = z = \frac{N_r \cdot H^2_{(!)}}{\overset{\shortmid}{N} \cdot P}$$

$$\text{height} = H_a = C_* \overset{\shortmid}{N} \left\{ \ln\left(1 + \frac{a}{A}\right) - 0.386 \right\}$$

$$\text{maximum volume} = M_{max} = k \cdot H \cdot N'^W$$

$$\text{basal area b.h.} = G = \left[\frac{\pi}{4} \prod^2 \cdot P \right] N'^W \left(1 - \frac{X}{H} \right)^2$$

$$\text{diameter b.h.} = d = \frac{\prod}{N'^{\frac{W}{2}}} \sqrt{x} \, (H - X) \, \frac{2}{(z + 1)}$$

and so on.

Chapter VII

GROWTH AS A FUNCTION OF COMPACTNESS FACTOR

As a result of thinning, the forest canopy is subjected to some loosening; therefore the crown-contact appears, to a greater or lesser degree, to be broken. The trees that remain in the stand react by growing more intensively; their crowns develop, and after a certain period the crown canopy closes.

Now to answer the question: What is the value of the compactness factor x after n years from the thinning, when the height of stand increases by:

$$\Delta H = H_{(a+n)} - H_a$$

The volume of a fully stocked compact stand is equal to:

$$M_{max} = k \cdot N^{'w} \cdot H \tag{16}$$

and the volume of a partially stocked one at an age a:

$$M_{(a)} = k \cdot x_a \cdot N^{'w} \cdot H_a \tag{16a}$$

where:

x_a = compactness factor at the age of a years

because from the definition:

$$x = \frac{M}{M_{max}}$$

During the interval of time n the compactness factor will increase from the value x_a to the value $x_{(a+n)}$.

It is known that:

$$0 \leq x \leq 1$$

Assume that the rapidity of increase of this factor is proportional to the product of the actual magnitude of the value x and the difference between this value and its limiting value of 1.0.

This is a principle of biological growth that was described by Robertson (cited from Walther, 1928, and Łomnicki, 1935). Thus the growth of the value x is expressed by the first derivative of x:

$$x' = K_o \cdot x \, (1 - x) \tag{(}$$

where K_o is a coefficient of proportionality expressing the rate of increase and x' is rapidity of growth of the value of x.

As the compactness factor x is a function of the time after thinning, and the height (H) is also a function of the time, then the growth of volume (ΔM) shall be expressed by a formula differentiating equation (16a) with respect to time:

$$\frac{\delta M}{\delta a} = \Delta M = k \cdot \overset{!}{N}^w \cdot \left[\Delta H \cdot x_a + H_a \cdot x_a \cdot K_o \cdot (1 - x_a) \right] \tag{(}$$

or in more convenient form:

$$\Delta M = k \cdot \overset{!}{N}^w \cdot H_a \cdot x_a \cdot \left[\frac{\Delta H}{H_a} + \frac{x_a \cdot K_o \cdot (1 - x_a)}{x_a} \right] \tag{(}$$

Using the principle about ecological saturation of stand, to wit:

$$\frac{M_{(a+n)}}{H_{(a+n)}} = \frac{M_a}{H_a} \tag{(}$$

one gets the equation:

$$\frac{M_{(a+n)}}{M_{max(a+n)} \cdot \dfrac{H_a}{H_{(a+n)}}} = \frac{M_a + \Delta M}{M_{max(a)}} \tag{(}$$

$$= \frac{k \cdot \overset{w}{N'} \cdot H_a \cdot x_a + k \cdot \overset{w}{N'} \cdot H_a \cdot x_a \left[\frac{\Delta H}{H_a} + K_o \cdot (1 - x_a) \right]}{k \cdot \overset{w}{N'} \cdot H_a}$$

$$= x_a \cdot \left[1 + \frac{\Delta H}{H_a} + K_o \cdot (1 - x_a) \right] \tag{31}$$

Thus:

$$x_{(a+n)} = \frac{M_{(a+n)}}{M_{max(a+n)}} = x_a \frac{H_a}{H_{(a+n)}} \left[1 + \frac{\Delta H}{H_a} + K_o \cdot (1 - x_a) \right] \tag{32}$$

But as:

$$1 + \frac{\Delta H}{H_a} = \frac{H_a + \Delta H}{H_a} = \frac{H_{(a+n)}}{H_a} \tag{33}$$

Thus:

$$x_{(a+n)} = x_a \cdot \left[1 + \frac{H_a}{H_{(a+n)}} \cdot K_o \cdot (1 - x_a) \right] \tag{34}$$

The term K_o must be considered as a factor of natural possibility of growth or, in other words, as a factor of rate of increase. As this possibility diminishes with age of stand then it may be imputed with a great degree of probability that:

$$K_o = \frac{H_{(a+n)}}{H_a} \cdot K_g \tag{35}$$

Thus is obtained:

$$x_{(a+n)} = x_a \cdot \left[1 + K_g \cdot (1 - x_a) \right] \tag{36}$$

or the same equation in another form:

$$x_{(a+n)} = x_a \cdot \left[(1 + K_g) - K_g \cdot x_a \right] \tag{37}$$

Experimental material concerning Scots pine stands indicates that the value of K_g varies from 0 to about 1, with the mean value about

0.7. Thus the formula for Scots pine stands may be expressed as follows:

$$x_{(a+n)} = x_a \ (1.7 - 0.7 \ x_a)$$

(3

This is the well-known formula of Gehrhardt (1930).

Intending to check this formula, as well as the validity of formula (16), the author has used some experimental material published by N. P. Georgievski (1948) and by Eytingen (1946) concerning Scots pine stands in Europe.

The results, presented in Table 17, point out that in this matter the role of crowding is quite invisible. Furthermore, the mean value of K_g is nearly equal to Gehrhardt's 0.7 for Scots pine stands. But the vacillation of this value is rather remarkable. It may a priori be forecast that no doubt the weather conditions during the period of observations affect the value of K_g, and it may also be suspected that the kind of thinning performs a certain role here. But there is a more important factor -- the accuracy of measurement.

Consider the influence of an error in measuring compactness factor on the result of calculation of the value of K_g.

Assume that the error of estimation of x is only ± 5 per cent; then the value of K_g may be as follows:

$$K_g = \frac{\dfrac{x_{(a+n)} \ (1 \pm 0.05)}{x_a \ (1 \pm 0.05)} - 1}{1 - x_a \ (1 \pm 0.05)}$$

TABLE 17.   Calculation of the value of K_g in Gehrhardt's formula for
Scots pine in Europe.   Data taken from Georgievski (1948) and Eytingen
(1946).   Values of K_g computed by use of formula (36).

Paper used	Year	Age a	Height H meters	Crowding factor z	Actual vol. M_r cu. m.	Submaximal vol. M_{smax} */ cu. m.	Compactness x	K_g
Georgievski	1930	26	9.5	2.1	189	259	0.73	
(1948)	1939	35	11.2	2.2	260	307	0.85	0.59
$\overset{\iota}{N}$ = 36.0	1930	26	9.7	2.0	154	259	0.60	
	1939	35	11.6	1.8	228	307	0.74	0.58
Thinned from	1930	26	9.8	2.1	142	259	0.55	
below.	1939	35	11.7	1.7	218	307	0.71	0.65
M_r includes	1930	26	10.0	2.2	123	259	0.48	
branches.	1939	35	12.1	1.3	210	307	0.68	0.81
	1930 mean =		9.7					
	1939 mean =		11.7					
Eytingen		24	9.8	0.48	87.1	239	0.36	
(1946)		35	15.0	0.73	199.7	358	0.56	0.86
$\overset{\iota}{N}$ = 40.0		24	10.2	0.45	105.4	239	0.44	
		35	15.2	0.85	207.4	358	0.58	0.57
Not thinned.		24	10.1	0.52	104.0	239	0.44	
		35	15.0	1.12	210.2	358	0.59	0.61

M_r includes
   trunks   Age 24 mean = 10.0   Mean K_g value = 0.67
   only.   Age 35 mean = 15.0

*/ Computed from formula (18).   For Georgievski's data, M_{smax} =
4.45 $\sqrt[\Gamma]{N}$ H, and for Eytingen's data, M_{smax} = 4.45 $\sqrt[\Gamma]{N}$ H(0.85), since
volumes in the latter publication represent trunks only.

And it may also happen that:

$$K_{g1} = \frac{\dfrac{x_{(a+n)} \cdot 1.05}{x_a \, 0.95} - 1}{1 - x_a \, 0.95} \tag{38a}$$

and:

$$K_{g_2} = \frac{\dfrac{x_{(a+n)}\ 0.95}{x_a\ 1.05} - 1}{1 - x_a\ 1.05}$$

Depending on the accuracy of measurements and on the value of x_a, one may in fact get values of K_g differing from the true value of 0.7 and accompanied by an error of $\pm$ 50 per cent or more.

Taking the data from Table 17 for the third plot reported by Georgievski and assuming that errors of 5 per cent in measuring x were made, x_a being 5 per cent too low, and $x_{(a+n)}$ being 5 per cent too high, then the value of K_g, computed from equation (38a), would be 0.90, compared to the tabular value of 0.65 -- an error of 54 per cent!

Unfortunately it is not possible to consider the influence of weather or kind of thinning on the value of K_g. But one conclusion must be made after the above remarks: Investigation of the question needs especially careful experiments. For this purpose stationary plots are not suitable because, for the distinct definition of the volume growth, it is necessary to cut out all trees on the plot.

As such experimental materials for loblolly pine stands were not at the author's disposal, he was forced to use what was available. The problem was first investigated by use of similar material for Scots pine stands in Europe, as Gehrhardt's formula was based on European Scots pine stands. Gehrhardt's formula was developed from studies of growth in total volume of stem and limbs down to a very small diameter and has been checked closely by the use of basal area of all trees one inch and larger in diameter as a unit of measure of stocking.

W. A. Duerr (1938), by means of increment cores taken on plots,

obtained Gehrhardt's constant K_g for jack pine (<u>Pinus</u> <u>banksiana</u> Lamb.)

stands equal to 0.6 without any serious vacillations (from 0.53 to

0.63). In his study Gehrhardt's constant was calculated for each group

of understocked plots and related to the group of plots of high density,

which was considered normal because, as pointed out by Duerr, Gehr-

hardt's formula is applicable in practice to any type of yield table if

only the proper constant is used. The value of this constant (K_g) as a

rule is treated by many authors as an indicator of tolerance of the spe-

cies. No doubt this number expresses a potential capacity of reaction

of volume growth after the loosening of the forest canopy. If this con-

stant is used as a characteristic of a species, it can be employed only

in connection with an approximately normal yield table. This condition

is also pointed out by Duerr. No doubt the most objective base of com-

parison of the compactness of a stand is the maximum obtainable volume

per surface unit.

For loblolly pine stands in Louisiana, the author calculated the

value of Gehrhardt's K_g using observations recorded at 10-year intervals

by W. F. Mann, Jr., Southern Forest Experiment Station, Alexandria,

Louisiana, and presented by him in progress reports entitled "Mayes

Thinning Study, December 8, 1950," and "Castor Thinning Study, February

1, 1951." The results of calculation are presented in Table 18.

This part of the work is interesting from a methodical point of

view: Using different scientific generalizations, such as Robertson's

growth law, Suchecki's principle about ecological saturation of the

stand, and the author's equation of maximum obtainable volume, one

TABLE 18. Calculation of the value of K_g in Gehrhardt's formula for loblolly pine in Louisiana. Data supplied by W. F. Mann, Jr., Southern Forest Experiment Station.

Locality and kind of thinning	Year	Age a (years)	Av. ht. domi- nants $H_{(!)}$	Site indi- cator N	Total vol.*/ M_r (cu. ft.)	Sub- maximal vol.**/ (cu. ft.)	Compact- ness factor x	K_g
Mayes;	1915	22	52	32.4	1654	3407	0.485	
heavy	1925	32	62	31.4	2509	4121	0.609	0.50
	1925	32	62	31.4	2311	4121	0.561	
	1935	42	67	30.2	3048	4425	0.689	0.52
	1935	42	67	30.2	2256	4425	0.510	
	1946	53	81	30.9	3334	5544	0.601	0.36
Mayes;	1935	42	67	30.2	2585	4425	0.584	
light	1946	53	79	30.5	3707	5352	0.693	0.45
Castor;	1920	26	69	34.0	2510	4850	0.518	
heavy	1930	36	85	34.5	4639	6176	0.751	0.93
	1930	36	85	34.5	3836	6176	0.621	
	1940	46	96	34.2	5591	7040	0.794	0.74
	1935	41	90	34.1	4637	6546	0.708	
	1946	52	102	34.3	6839	7537	0.907	0.96
Castor;	1920	26	71	34.6	3284	5054	0.650	
light	1930	36	84	34.1	5307	6064	0.875	0.99
	1935	41	90	34.1	5453	6546	0.833	
	1946	52	109	35.4	8250	8227	1.003	1.22
Castor;	1920	26	64	33.4	3374	4412	0.765	
unthinned	1930	36	80	33.6	4979	5703	0.873	0.60
	1930	36	80	33.6	4979	5703	0.873	
	1940	46	92	33.6	6416	6661	0.963	0.81
	1935	41	86	33.5	5614	6171	0.910	
	1946	52	103	34.3	7259	7618	0.953	0.53

Mean = 0.72

*/ Computed from merchantable volume by use of converting factors based on average d.b.h.

**/ Computed from formula (16b), where k = 13.8.

finally arrives at the well-known Gehrhardt formula.

From a practical point of view, this consideration is not less important: To predict the value of the average diameter after n years between thinnings, one must know not only the crowding or number of trees per surface unit, and the height in the future but also must predict the value of the compactness factor or volume in the future. Gehrhardt's formula may serve as a useful tool in this matter.

Chapter VIII

CROWN-LENGTH RATIO AS AN INDEX OF DEGREE OF CROWDING

In the first chapter the use of crown-length ratio as a criterion of normality of crowding in a forest stand was suggested. However, in the next chapters only formula (1) was used as a measure of normality of crowding. This procedure is understandable, as it is well known that measurement of crown length is laborious, inaccurate, and somewhat subjective.

In spite of these disadvantages, the problem of crown-length ratio must be considered, because it is one of the important problems of forest ecology in general, as well as the fact that it casts a great dea of light on thinning procedure in practical silviculture.

Crown-length ratio is indicated by the expression:

$$\frac{H - h_*}{H}$$

where:

> H = height of tree (from the level of the earth to the tip of the tree)
>
> $H - h_*$ = length of tree crown

What does "length of tree crown" mean? Various authors define crown-length differently. For instance in the practice of the Southern Forest Experiment Station in Alexandria, Louisiana, this length means th length from the top of a tree to the last whorl of at least two living

branches of normal size (i.e. very small living branches below that

point are disregarded).

But another question arises concerning the notion of crown-

length ratio: how to compute an effective average value for the whole

of a forest stand. In the practice of the above-mentioned station it is

the average value of crown-lengths of ten dominant and codominant trees,

divided by the mean value of the heights of these trees. In the various

countries there are different practices prevailing for these computa-

tions. No doubt such conventions are merely artificial, but it is pos-

sible to devise certain natural, and at the same time (to a certain

degree) more objective, ones.

Regardless of how one may comprehend the crown-length ratio, it

is known that:

Crown-length ratio	Crowding factor
$\rightarrow 1$	$\rightarrow 0$
$L < \dfrac{H - h_*}{H} < 1$	$1 > z > 0$
L	1
$< L$	$z > 1$
$\rightarrow 0$	$\rightarrow \infty$

where the magnitude L expresses the crown-length ratio in a fully

stocked stand and in conditions of the normal crowding factor z. Thus

the definition of L is as follows:

$$\frac{H - h_*}{H} = L$$

when z = 1 and x = 1. This number is called normal crown-length ratio.

From the above-given course of development of crown-length ratio as a function of crowding factor it may be concluded that:

$$\frac{H - h_*}{H} = L^{f(z)}$$

provided that:

$$f(z) = 0$$

when:

$$z = 0$$

One of the possibilities when this condition is satisfied is that:

$$\frac{H - h_*}{H} = L^{\sqrt{z}}$$

But this solution may be treated only as a first approximation, because it is obvious that in conditions of the same crowding factor a different crown-length may exist, depending on the volume of standing trees or, in other words, depending on the actual compactness factor.

This idea may be expressed as follows:

$$\frac{H - h_*}{H} = L^{f(x) \cdot \sqrt{z}}$$

Considering this problem one cannot fail to understand that when:

x	f(x)
1	1
< 1	$0 < f(x) < 1$

Among the numerous solutions of the question of how to express the function of x, it is simple enough and quite possible that

$$f(x) = \frac{2\sqrt{x}}{x+1} \tag{43}$$

Thus is obtained the equation:

$$\frac{H - h_*}{H} = L^{\frac{2\sqrt{x}}{x+1}\sqrt{z}} \tag{44}$$

Using measurements made by H. Enghardt in the Alexander State Forest (Southern Forest Experiment Station, Alexandria, Louisiana) in 1959 the author arrived at the calculations presented in Table 19. The same subject is presented in Figure 11.

As can be seen, the last formula applied to loblolly pine stands has the normal crown-length ratio:

$$L = 0.31$$

The standard error of estimate for the formula is equal to 7 per cent. This is no small value. One may expect that this deviation results first from the subjectivity of the notion of crown-length used, and second, from the method of choosing from the stand single trees that are not completely representative of the ecological conditions of the community of trees.

Knowing the method used, one may estimate the magnitude of the error in measurements of the crown-length ratio. But before this estimation it is necessary to consider the possibility of amending existing methods of computation of crown-length.

It seems very logical that the crown-length is the length from the tree top to the base of the last whorl of living branches. This case exists only when the crown is quite regular, as a result of uniform shade by crowns of neighboring trees. If normally a whorl contains six

TABLE 19. Comparison of crown-length ratio with crowding and compactness factors in a loblolly pine stand on the Alexander State Forest, Louisiana. Basic data obtained from W. F. Mann, Jr., Alexandria Research Center, Southern Forest Experiment Station. Measurements made in 1958 at age 30, five years after the 1953 thinning and before the 1958 thinning.

Plot #	No. trees per acre N	Tot. vol. ins. bk. per acre (cu. ft.) [1/] M_T	Av. dom. ht. trees H	Site indi-cator $\frac{}{N}$	Crowd-ing factor z	Max. vol. ins. bk. per acre (cu. ft.) M_{smax}	Compact-ness factor x	Exponent in form. (44) $\frac{2\sqrt{xz}}{x+1}$	Crown-length ratio [2/] $\frac{H - h_*}{H}$
3	270	2073	57.5	31.0	.66	3775	.549	.778	.410
6	270	2302	57.0	30.9	.65	3732	.617	.783	.384
2	270	2666	56.6	30.7	.65	3644	.732	.797	.404
5	410	2436	54.3	30.2	.92	3427	.711	.945	.376
1	480	2677	56.9	30.8	1.16	3688	.726	1.064	.392
4	430	2486	57.4	31.0	1.05	3775	.659	1.002	.359
5	240	2350	62.5	32.0	0.67	4210	.558	.784	.377
10	260	2132	56.3	30.6	.62	3601	.592	.760	.421
15	190	2279	68.6	33.0	.62	4704	.484	.737	.421
20	170	2201	64.1	32.2	.50	4309	.511	.669	.409
1	230	2406	62.7	32.0	.65	4210	.571	.775	.396
4	350	2433	56.5	30.7	.83	3644	.668	.892	.362
6	290	2740	57.0	30.9	.70	3732	.734	.827	.356
11	310	2398	55.3	30.3	.72	3470	.691	.833	.389
14	330	2210	59.7	31.4	.86	3949	.560	.891	.377
16	230	2851	67.0	32.8	.72	4605	.619	.825	.396
19	260	2161	64.3	32.2	.77	4309	.502	.828	.394
3	220	3265	66.2	32.6	.68	4506	.725	.814	.343
8	210	2772	72.3	33.6	.75	5000	.554	.830	.416
13	320	2631	57.4	31.0	.78	3775	.697	.869	.382
18	230	2272	70.7	33.4	.79	4901	.464	.828	.366
2	280	2620	58.0	31.0	.70	3775	.694	.823	.376
7	300	2436	59.2	31.2	.77	3862	.631	.855	.373
17	210	2809	66.2	32.5	.65	4457	.630	.785	.376
12	300	2459	58.1	31.0	.75	3775	.651	.845	.351
4P	130	2466	69.2	33.1	.43	4753	.519	.621	.427
4	170	2389	64.0	32.2	.49	4309	.554	.669	.461
8	170	2343	62.9	32.1	.48	4259	.550	.663	.420
12	170	2306	61.9	31.8	.47	4123	.559	.656	.388
16	170	2366	62.7	32.0	.48	4210	.562	.665	.420
3P	190	2758	60.6	31.6	.50	4036	.683	.695	.419
3	240	2709	61.4	31.7	.65	4080	.664	.790	.432
7	220	2582	64.0	32.2	.64	4309	.599	.774	.407
11	200	2823	61.6	31.7	.55	4080	.692	.729	.433
15	220	2631	62.4	32.0	.61	4210	.625	.760	.401

[1/] Converted from merchantable cubic volume by a ratio varying with average stand diameter.
[2/] Based on average of 10 dominant or codominant trees per 0.1-acre plot.

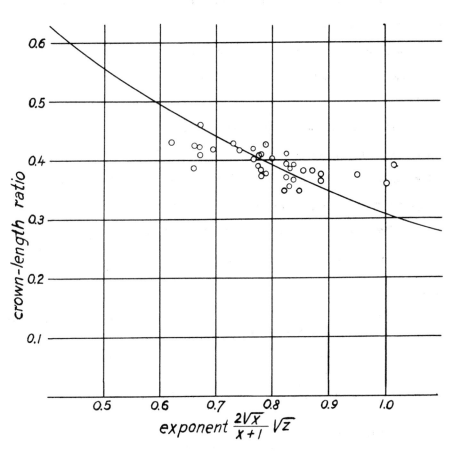

FIGURE 11. Crown-length ratio as a function of crowding (z) and compactness (x) factors in loblolly pine stands in Louisiana.

branches and one branch (of the size of the remaining living branches) in the last whorl is dead, it may be assumed that the crown-length is less by 1/6 of the value of the difference in length between the last whorl and the preceding one. If two branches in the last living whorl are dead, the effective value of crown-length is less by 2/6 of the value of one year's height growth during the time of formation of the last whorl.

If five branches in the last living whorl are dead or, in other words, if there is only one live branch in this "whorl," the effective value of crown-length is less by 5/6 of the value of that particular height growth. This case is illustrated in Figure 12.

Therefore this method may be expressed by the formula:

$$H - h_e = (H - h_1) - \frac{n}{6} (\Delta H_1)$$

where:

$H - h_e$ = effective crown length or actual length of crown when it is complete

n = number of dead branches in the lowest whorl of the crown

$H - h_1$ = actual length from the tip to the last incomplete whorl

ΔH_1 = the height growth during the time of formation of the lowest whorl of the crown

These symbols are explained in Figure 12.

Of course, when the normal number of branches in each whorl for a certain species is other than 6, this magnitude must be changed in the last formula.

Concerning the computation of mean value of crown-length ratio for the whole stand, it seems rational to take under consideration model

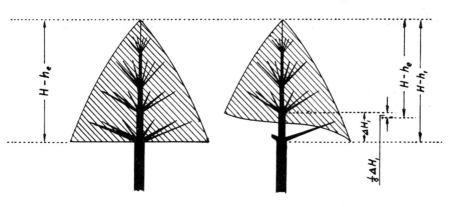

FIGURE 12. Diagram showing the effective crown-length ratio (H - h$_e$).

trees (sample trees) from a certain number of diameter classes, each including the same number of trees, instead of measuring only dominants.
This argument is based on the fact that the role of crowding in crown-
length formation is dominant compared to the role of the compactness factor, which is deduced from formula (44).

Taking under consideration the above discussion the error in
measurement of crown-length ratio may be estimated when the method that
was applied in computing Table 19 is used. If it is assumed that $H - h_1$
$= H - h_e$, an error may be committed whereby in a case of $H = 60$ feet,
annual height growth $\Delta H_1 = 1.6$ feet, and $L = 0.33$ it may be found:

$$\frac{\dfrac{H - h_*}{H} - \dfrac{(H - h_1) - \dfrac{4}{6.}(\Delta H_1)}{H}}{\dfrac{(H - h_1) - \dfrac{4}{6}(\Delta H_1)}{H}} \cdot 100 = \frac{0.330 - \dfrac{20 - 1.1}{60}}{0.315} = \frac{0.015}{0.315}$$

$= 4.8\%$

If one deals with standing trees and commits an error of height
measurement equal to $\pm$ 2 per cent, the total error in single cases may
reach 5.3 per cent. But a great error is committed by measuring atypical
trees to determine crown-length ratios of separate trees. This normally
is equal at least to 10 per cent with regard to the mean value, as was
determined with use of data presented by Kunze (1918).

Therefore, the standard error of crown-length ratio calculated a
equal to $\pm$ 7 per cent with regard to the results of the formula may be
considered as a quite understandable value of error of the method used.

An interesting experiment concerning this problem is found in a paper by P. A. Briegleb (1952). He studied three Douglas-fir stands, all on land of site quality III. They had very contrasting histories, as can be seen by the stand profiles (Figure 13). Number of trees per acre and crowding conditions varied widely (Table 20).

Using this valuable experimental material I intend to demonstrate how the crown-length ratio may be used in a scientific investigation concerning normality for approaching the definition of the normal number of trees per surface unit as well as to check formula (41).

It may be seen in Table 20 that stands "A" and "C" are in almost the same crowding conditions, because the crown-length ratios in both stands have nearly the same values. Also evident is the fact that stand "B" is approximately four times as crowded as stand "C." This becomes evident when one compares number of trees per acre. Both stands are of the same age, but stand "C" is taller due to better site quality. However, the ratio of crowding between these two stands may be precisely defined if one considers that:

$$\frac{N'_C}{N'_B} \approx \frac{H_C}{H_B} \tag{46}$$

This is evident from equation (7a), as both stands have the same age. Thus:

$$\frac{N'_C}{N'_B} = \frac{93}{90} = 1.03$$

$$N'_C = 1.03 \, N'_B \tag{46a}$$

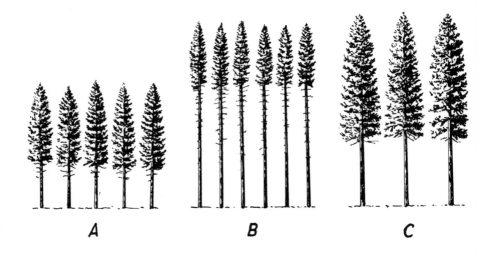

FIGURE 13. Three contrasting Douglas-fir stands after thinning (from Briegleb, 1952).

TABLE 20. Stand characteristics of three contrasting Douglas-fir stands
after thinning (from Briegleb, 1952).

Designation of stand	Historical remarks	Age a (yrs.)	Av. diameter b.h. d (in.)	Av. ht. H	Av. crown-length ratio $\dfrac{H - h_*}{H}$	Act. no. of trees per acre N_r	Stand intensity M $\dfrac{H}{(sq.ft.)}$	Compactness factor with regard to stand B x
A	First thinned at age 20; 6th thinning just completed.	35	10	60	0.622	206	48	0.545
B	Overdense to age 55; first thinning just completed.	55	10	90	0.352	372	88	1.000
C	First thinned at age 20; 12th thinning just completed.	55	17.5	93	0.627	85	53	0.602

If formula (12a) is used, the value $\overset{\shortmid}{N}$ may be computed from the ratio:

$$\frac{d_c}{d_B} = \frac{c\sqrt{\dfrac{M_c}{H_c}} \; \dfrac{1}{\sqrt{\overset{\shortmid}{N_c}}} \; (H_c - 4.5) \cdot 2 \cdot \left[\dfrac{N_B \cdot H_B^2}{\overset{\shortmid}{N_B} \cdot 43560} + 1\right]}{c\sqrt{\dfrac{M_B}{H_B}} \; \dfrac{1}{\sqrt{\overset{\shortmid}{N_B}}} \; (H_B - 4.5) \cdot 2 \cdot \left[\dfrac{N_c \cdot H_c^2}{\overset{\shortmid}{N_c} \cdot 43560} + 1\right]}$$

then:

$$1.75 = \sqrt{\frac{53}{88}} \; \sqrt{\frac{N_B'}{1.03 \cdot N_B'}} \; \frac{88.5}{85.5} \cdot \frac{\left[\dfrac{69.1}{N_B'} + 1 \right]}{\left[\dfrac{16.9}{1.03 \, N_B'} + 1 \right]}$$

$$2.2 = \frac{\dfrac{69.1}{N_B'} + 1}{\dfrac{16.4}{N_B'} + 1}$$

$$N_B' = 27.1$$

Then from formula (46a):

$$N_C' = 1.03 \cdot 27.1 = 27.9$$

When the values of site indicators N' are known, crowding factors of both stands may be computed from the equation:

$$z = \frac{N \cdot H^2}{N' \cdot 43560}$$

$$z_C = \frac{16.9}{N_C'} = \frac{16.9}{27.9} = 0.605$$

$$z_B = \frac{69.1}{N_B'} = \frac{69.1}{27.1} = 2.55$$

Then it may be assumed:

$$z_A = 0.605$$

Since the values of crown-length ratios are known from the experiment and the values of crowding factors are already known, one may calculate the value of L in formula (44), treating the ratio of the actual stand intensity to the stand intensity of the fully stocked stand B as a compactness factor (x). This treatment is quite rational, as in fact the compactness factor is equal to this ratio if the site indicators of stands do not differ greatly.

$$x = \frac{M}{M_{max}} = \frac{\dfrac{M}{H}}{\dfrac{M_{max}}{H}} = \frac{x \cdot k \cdot N'^{W}}{k \cdot N'^{W}} = x$$

As

$$\frac{H - h_*}{H} = L$$

Thus the crown-length ratio will be:

1. in the stand A equal to $L^{\frac{2\sqrt{0.545}}{1.545}\sqrt{0.605}}$

in the stand B equal to $L^{\sqrt{2.55}}$

in the stand C equal to $L^{\frac{2\sqrt{0.602}}{1.602}\sqrt{0.605}}$

Using data concerning stand B one gets:

$$\sqrt{2.55} \cdot \log L = \log 0.352$$

$$\log L = \frac{\log 0.352}{\sqrt{2.55}}$$

$$L_B = 0.52$$

Using data concerning the stand C:

$$\frac{2\sqrt{0.602}}{1.602} \sqrt{0.605} \log L = \log 0.627$$

$$\log L = \frac{(\log 0.627)\ 1.602 \cdot \sqrt{0.605}}{2\sqrt{0.602}}$$

$$L_C = 0.54$$

The mean value $(\frac{1}{2})(L_B + L_C) = 0.53$ may be treated as a value for computing the length-crown ratio in stand A:

$$\frac{H - h*}{H} = 0.53^{\frac{2\sqrt{0.545}}{1.545}} \sqrt{0.605}$$

$$\frac{H - h_*}{H} = 0.625$$

while by measurement it was obtained as 0.622.

Thus is given an evident example of how precisely the values of site indicators and the crowding factors may be defined, if one has at his disposal some validly performed experiments.

As the value of the expression $\frac{2\sqrt{x}}{x + 1}$ varies only a little in the range of x from 1 to 0.6, and actually nearly equals to 1, for practical purposes formula (41) may be used. Figure 14 presents a graph of crown-length ratio as a function of crowding factor for certain values of z.

As this graph is based on an insufficient number of observations, it does not pretend to indicate any detailed values for separate species, but only presents an idea of what future usefulness may be realized in the practice of silviculture in this way. As is seen in the graph, the value L presents an index of light-tolerance of species: in conditions of normal crowding for loblolly pine this index is between 0.30 and 0.35, while for Douglas-fir it lies between 0.50 and 0.55. It is quite understandable: the more tolerant the species, the larger the crown-length ratio for identical crowding conditions. Of course this

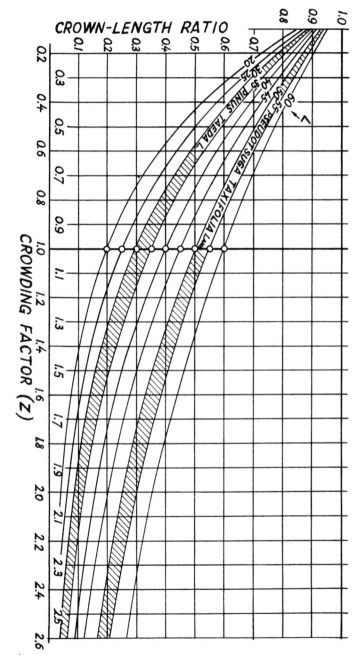

FIGURE 14. Crown-length ratio as a function of crowding factor for different values of L.

problem suggests some additional and very interesting questions -- for instance, the problem of the value of this index as a function of age and geophysical location. These problems belong to the future. The task of this chapter was to show a method for using crown-length to define the crowding factor as well as the site indicator and to show some prospects for the proposed method.

Chapter IX

APPLICATION OF THE THEORY TO FOREST PRACTICE

The theory presented in the preceding chapters has a direct application to the problem of choosing the proper degree or grade of thinning. To solve this problem, a decision must first be made as to the task of production. If one knows the laws of nature, the present condition of the stand, and sets definite, realistic production goals, he is able to realize those goals.

Since average stand diameter is a function of compactness, crowding factors, and stand height (formulas 14 and 19), present crowding and compactness conditions may be regulated, depending on the average stand diameter desired in the future. Treating the problem of thinning in this way, the production task is then expressed as the attainment of a certain average diameter and a certain compactness at a time n years after thinning done in a stand now at the age of a years. Then the first problem is the computation of the compactness factor x_a which must be obtained immediately after thinning.

Using Gehrhardt's formula the needed value of x_a may then be calculated, making use of the planned compactness factor $x_{(a+n)}$, which one wants to obtain after n years:

$$x_{(a+n)} = x_a \left[1 + K_g (1 - x_a) \right]$$ (36)

$$x_{(a+n)} = x_a (1 + K_g) - K_g \cdot x_a^2$$

115

$$x_a^2 - \left(\frac{1 + K_g}{K_g}\right) x_a + \frac{x_{(a+n)}}{K_g} = 0$$

As the value of $x_a \leq 1$, thus:

$$x_a = \frac{1 + K_g}{2 K_g} - \frac{1}{2} \sqrt{\left(\frac{1 + K_g}{K_g}\right)^2 - 4 \frac{x_{(a+n)}}{K_g}}$$ (

When $K_g = 0.7$, then:

$$x_a = 1.215 - \frac{1}{2} \sqrt{5.90 - 5.71 \, x_{(a+n)}}$$ (

In other words, to obtain in the future a compactness factor equal to $x_{(a+n)}$, one must reduce by thinning the present value of x to x_a, and this value of x_a is computable using formula (36a).

When the required present-day value of x_a has been calculated, the volume that should be removed in the thinning may be computed, using formulas (16a) and (19):

$$m_t = (x - x_a) \, k \cdot H \cdot \overset{\text{'}}{N} = (x - x_a) \, M_{smax}$$ (

where:

m_t = volume that should be removed by thinning

x = compactness factor before thinning at age a years

x_a = compactness factor after thinning at age a years

It must also be known how many trees should be removed from the stand in the thinning. For this information, there must be known the value of the crowding factor at the age (a+n) that will assure obtaining of the desired average stand diameter at this age. Since the relationship between average diameter, compactness factor, and crowding factor is expressed by formula (13a):

$$d_{(a+n)} = \frac{\Pi}{\sqrt[4]{N'}} \sqrt{x_{(a+n)}} \; (H_{(a+n)} - X) \frac{2}{z_{(a+n)} + 1} \tag{13a}$$

the value of the crowding factor z at the age (a+n) may be calculated:

$$z_{(a+n)} = \frac{2\Pi}{d_{(a+n)} \sqrt[4]{N'}} \sqrt{x_{(a+n)}} \; (H_{(a+n)} - X) - 1 \tag{48}$$

If the necessary future value of $z_{(a+n)}$ is ascertained, the number of

trees $N_{(a+n)}$ at the age (a+n) may be figured by use of formulas (4) and

(1):

$$z_{(a+n)} = \frac{N_{(a+n)} \cdot H^2_{(a+n)}}{N' \cdot 43560} \tag{49}$$

$$N_{(a+n)} = z_{(a+n)} \cdot N' \frac{43560}{H^2} \tag{50}$$

Then, if the actual present number of trees before thinning equals N_r,

the number of trees to be removed (n_t) is computable as a difference:

$$n_t = N_r - N_{(a+n)} \tag{51}$$

Summarizing, the theory which is presented here enables one to

define the degree or grade of thinning using two magnitudes, m_t and n_t.

For example, for a certain loblolly pine stand the characteris-

tics of·stand structure are presented as follows:

1. From actual stand measurements:

    a. age (a) = 36 years

    b. av. ht. dominants $(H_{(!)})$ = 85 feet

    c. no. trees per acre (N_r) = 184

    d. av. d.b.h. (d_r) = 11.4 inches

    e. vol. per acre = 4500 cu. ft.

2. Desired stand measurements n = 10 years hence:

    a. av. d.b.h. $d_{(a+n)}$ = 13.5 inches

    b. compactness factor $x_{(a+n)}$ = 0.80

3. From graph, Figure 10:

    a. site indicator $(\overset{\shortmid}{N})$ = 34.4

    b. av. ht. dominants at age 46 years $H_{(a+n)}$ = 97 feet

4. Computed by formulas:

    a. submaximum vol. at age 36 $M_{smax} = 13.8\sqrt{\overset{\shortmid}{N}}\,\dfrac{(H - 4.5)^2}{H}$
       = 6176 cu. feet (form. 16b)

    b. submaximum vol. at age 46 M_{smax} =

$$13.8\sqrt{\overset{\shortmid}{N}}\,\frac{\left(H_{(a+n)} - 4.5\right)^2}{H_{(a+n)}} = 7146 \text{ cu. feet}$$

    c. compactness factor before thinning (x) = 4500/6176= 0.73

    d. compactness factor after thinning (x_a) = 0.64 (formula 36b)

    e. vol. removed by thinning (m_t) = 556 cu. ft. (formula 47)

    f. crowding factor at age 46 $(z_{(a+n)})$ =

$$\frac{2 \times 0.40}{13.5 \times 2.4}\,\sqrt{0.8} \times 92.5 - 1 \text{ (formula 48)} = 1.03$$

    g. no. trees at age 46 $N_{(a+n)}$ = 164 (formula 50)

    h. no. trees removed by thinning n_t = 20 (formula 51)

After these computations one may present the stand characteristics in the following assemblage:

	Age a (yrs.)	Av. ht. (dom.) H (feet)	Site indi-cator $\overset{\shortmid}{N}$	No. of trees per acre N	Crowd-ing factor z	Av. d.b.h. d (in.)	Volume M (cu.ft.)	Compact-ness factor x
Before thin-ning	36	85	34.4	184	0.89	11.4	4500	0.73
After thin-ning	36	85	34.4	164	0.79	-	3944	0.64
After n = 10 years	46	97	34.4	164	1.03	13.5	5717	0.80

The theory appears to be a practical tool for predicting the separate characteristics of a forest stand as functions of a postulated task of production. By using this theory it is possible to formulate consciously the structure of a stand, systematically, step by step. To perform these calculations one must know the values of $\overset{\shortmid}{N}$, k, and Π, which must be computed using the method presented in Chapters V and VII. Of course, computations of these coefficients are not easy matters, but they must be defined only once for the species under consideration.

In some cases when the values of coefficients $\overset{\shortmid}{N}$, k, and Π cannot be computed, the formula may be used:

$$d = \varsigma \sqrt{\frac{M}{H \cdot N}} \left(1 - \frac{X}{H}\right) \tag{22a}$$

to determine the thinning grade. After transformation, the last formula becomes, in the system of measurements used in the United States:

$$N_{(a+n)} = \varsigma^2 \frac{M_{(a+n)}}{H_{(a+n)} \cdot d_{(a+n)}^2} \left(1 - \frac{4.5}{H_{(a+n)}}\right)^2$$

where the magnitudes $M_{(a+n)}$ and $d_{(a+n)}$ are planned values, and the value of $n_t = N_r - N_{(a+n)}$ may be defined. Using formula (36a) and suitable yield tables, one may calculate x_a, and then m_t, analogously to the preceding case. Although the computation of the value of ς is very easy, using formula (22), this computational method gives no measure of crowding factor.

But if it is desired to regulate validly the structure of a stand, the importance of crowding factor cannot be neglected. Although the knowledge of total production of wood, i.e. stems and branches, is necessary to solve the most important theoretical problems of forest production, the production of stems is currently the task of practical forest production. Therefore, in thinning operations one cannot lose sight of maximum possible volume of stems per surface unit. This volume can be estimated:

$$M_s = \frac{\pi}{4} d^2 \cdot N_r \cdot H \cdot F_s$$

where

M_s = volume of stems per surface unit

F_s = average stem form factor for the stand, form factor being
defined as $\dfrac{\text{volume of tree}}{\text{volume of cylinder}}$

N_r = actual number of trees per surface unit

The actual number of trees may be expressed in terms of crowding factor and normal number per surface unit, and simultaneously the diameter may be stated in terms of height and crowding factor:

$$M_s = \frac{\pi}{4} \cdot \frac{\prod^2}{\sqrt{N}} \cdot x \cdot (H - X)^2 \frac{4}{(z+1)^2} z \cdot \overset{\cdot}{N} \frac{P}{H^2} \cdot F_s$$

$$M_s = x(\pi \cdot \prod^2 \cdot P) \sqrt{N} \left(1 - \frac{X}{H}\right)^2 \cdot \left[\frac{z}{(z+1)^2}\right] H \cdot F_s \qquad (52)$$

Thus it is ascertained that volume of stems is evidently a function of crowding factor z, and this function (the expression between brackets) reaches a maximum when z = 1 (see Figure 15). Although the problem of stem form factor as a function of crowding factor has not yet been elaborated, it is known that the greater the crowding, the greater also the stem form factor; thus for values of z < 1, the volume of stems is for these values lower in comparison to the obtainable one.

Formula (52) describes the phenomenon of the dependence of actual volume of stems on crowding factor, compactness factor, site indicator, and height. Using this relation one may conclude that, all other things being equal, or when x, $\overset{\cdot}{N}$, and H are the same, the influence of crowding factor on volume of stems in a stand has no great importance; thus nearly the same final crop volume may be reached in conditions of crowding factor varying from 0.7 to 1.4, but in the first case a crop containing trees 1.4 times thicker than in the second case will be obtained. Therefore, in the planning of thinning grade one cannot neglect the crowding factor and, therefore, is obliged to try to use formula (13a) whenever possible.

There are some silvicultural problems included in the drainage of swamp lands and moorlands. As height growth is a function of site indicator, each change of soil-moisture conditions is reflected in this growth. One may always make a simple analysis of a curve of height

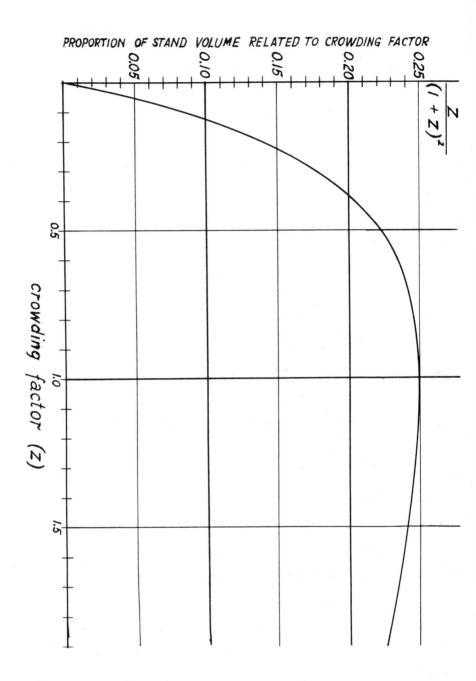

FIGURE 15. Influence of crowding factor on volume of stems in a stand.

growth in comparison to meteorological fluctuations and then draw conclusions about the possibility of increase of site indicator under the
influence of the change of moisture conditions accompanying a new system
of drainage canals. The possibility of defining the increase of site
indicator in a quantitative way enables definition of the value of
volume growth in the future after the realization of a drainage plan.
Presentation of this method requires so much explanation of the relationships between growth in volume and mass of leaves, between soil
moisture and site indicator, between transpiration and volume production
and so on, that a separate monograph is needed. It suffices here to
state that this method has been used in practice quite successfully.

   The theory may also be applied in forest regulation. Take under
consideration the so-called Austrian formula:

Annual cut = Annual increment

$$+ \; \frac{\text{Actual growing stock - Desired growing stock}}{\text{Adjustment period}}$$

The theory is helpful in defining the desired growing stock (using
formula 16), as well as in computing the increment. As it is known
that:

$$M_r = x \cdot k \cdot H \cdot \overset{'}{N^w} \tag{16a}$$

it is possible to calculate the increment, or volume growth (M), using
considerations given in Chapter VII.

$$\Delta M = \frac{\delta M}{\delta a} = (x \; k \cdot H \cdot \overset{'}{N^w})' = k \cdot \overset{'}{N^w} (x \cdot H)'$$

$$= k \cdot \overset{'}{N^w} (x_a \cdot \Delta H + \Delta x_a \cdot H_a) = k \cdot \overset{'}{N^w} \left[x_a \cdot \Delta H + K_o \cdot x_a \cdot (1 - x_a) H_a \right]$$

$$= k \cdot \overset{'}{N}{}^W \left[x_a \cdot \triangle H + \frac{H_{(a+n)}}{H_a} K_g \cdot x_a (1 - x_a) H_a \right]$$

$$= k \cdot \overset{'}{N}{}^W \cdot x_a \left[\triangle H + H_{(a+n)} \cdot K_g (1 - x_a) \right]$$

For each forest property to be regulated the mean values of $\overset{'}{N}$, $\overset{'}{N}{}^W$, x_a, and H_a may be calculated for all species represented, by separate age classes; then the volume growth in each class may be ascertained; and finally, after the addition of values of separate growths, it is possible to obtain the total increment for the whole property. The calculation is remarkably easier, more convenient, considerably more accurate, and less time-consuming than the methods now used in the practice of forest management.

Application of the theory in forest· management is such a broad subject that the presentation would require a special study and a separate monograph.

Chapter X

SUMMARY

Studies of the growth of even-aged forest stands led the author to the development of a theory of forest-stand dynamics. This theory contains two major hypotheses:

1. In pure, even-aged stands of a given species growing on land of identical site quality and under conditions of comparable competition for growing space, the number of trees per unit of land area is inversely proportional to the square of the mean height of the stand.

2. The average diameter breast high in a stand is directly proportional to the mean stand height reduced by the height of measurement of diameter and inversely proportional to a "crowding" factor enlarged by the value 1.

The following formulas express these hypotheses mathematically:

$$N = \overset{\prime}{N} \frac{P}{H^2}$$

and

$$d = \alpha(H - X) \frac{2}{z+1} = \alpha H \frac{2}{z+1} - \Delta$$

where:

N = normal number of trees per surface unit (acre or hectare)

P = surface unit (43,560 sq. ft. or 10,000 sq. m.)

H = mean height of stand (or of the dominant trees)

125

$\overset{\shortmid}{N}$ = site indicator (constant value for a site class)

d = average stand diameter breast high

X = breast height (generally 4.5 ft. or 1.3 m.)

$\triangle$ = constant for the species

α = coefficient of proportionality (depending on stand "compactness")

z = crowding factor = $\dfrac{\text{actual number of trees per surface unit}}{\text{normal number of trees per surface unit}}$

$= \dfrac{N_r}{N}$

The site indicator $\overset{\shortmid}{N}$ has a marked superiority in relation to other site indices used, as the term $\overset{\shortmid}{N}$ is represented in simple forms in important relationships among forest stand characteristics:

normal number of trees per P = $N = \overset{\shortmid}{N}\ \dfrac{P}{H^2}$

crowding factor = $z = \dfrac{N_r}{N} = \dfrac{N_r \cdot H^2}{\overset{\shortmid}{N} \cdot P}$

average diameter b.h. = $d = \dfrac{\prod}{\overset{\shortmid}{N}{}^{\frac{w}{2}}}\ \sqrt{x}\ (H - X)\ \dfrac{2}{z + 1}$

stand height at the age a = $H_a = C_x \overset{\shortmid}{N} \left\{ \ln\left(1 + \dfrac{a}{A}\right) - 0.386 \right\}$

coefficient of proportionality = $\alpha = c\sqrt{\dfrac{M_r}{H \cdot \overset{\shortmid}{N}}}$

maximum volume for a given stand height and site quality
= $M_{max} = k \cdot H \cdot \overset{\shortmid}{N}{}^w$

where:

x = compactness factor = $\dfrac{\text{actual volume per surface unit}}{\text{maximum volume per surface unit}}$

$= \dfrac{M_r}{M_{max}}$

a = age of stand

A = age of culmination of height growth (depending on site quality)

The numbers C_*, c, Δ, Π, k, and w are constant (or practically constant) for a species. Among coefficients there are these relationships:

$$c = \frac{\Pi}{\sqrt{k}}$$

$$\alpha = \frac{\Pi}{N^{\frac{w}{2}}}$$

$$k = \frac{\pi}{4}\,\Pi^2 \cdot \left(\frac{H-X}{H}\right)^2 F \cdot P$$

where F = stand form factor.

Using the hypotheses presented above, a formula was derived to predict the compactness factor $x_{(a+n)}$, i.e. the value of this factor n years after thinning done at the age of a years:

$$x_{(a+n)} = x_a \left[1 + K_g(1 - x_a)\right]$$

which is the well-known Gehrhardt formula.

Numerical values of these coefficients are as follows:

	X	Δ	Π	k	C_*	w	K_g (10 yrs.)
Scots pine (Europe) in metric system	1.3 m.	1.7 cm.	0.0309	4.45 (stems and branches)	0.5	0.5	0.7
Loblolly pine (America) in U.S. customary system	4.5 ft.	0.6 in.	0.40	13.8 (stems only)	1.64	0.5	0.7
in metric system	1.37 m.	1.5 cm.	0.03	4.18	-	0.5	0.7

A formula was developed for expressing average crown-length ratio as a function of crowding and compactness factors. This formula, for fully compact stands, is:

$$\text{crown-length ratio} = \frac{H - h_*}{H} = L^{\sqrt{z}}$$

where:

L = crown-length ratio in a stand with normal crowding factor ($z = 1$).

Tentatively the value of L was established as 0.3 for Scots pine and loblolly pine and 0.5 for Douglas fir.

The theory is in conformity with investigations of Baader and Zimmerle; with observations presented by Eytingen; with the conception of Khil'mi; as well as with formulas given by Köhler, Chisman and Schumacher, and Bistrup; with the spacing criterion of Gevorkiantz; Hummel's postulates; Suchecki's principle of ecological saturation of stand; a study by Briegleb; and construction of experimental formulas used by Simmons and Schnur, McKinney et al., Meyer, Lynch, and Gehrhardt; as well as with experimental material concerning Scots pine in Europe (published by Weise, Jedliński, Kunze) and the experimental material concerning loblolly pine in Louisiana (presented by Mann and Bateman).

The theory may be applied to many problems of forest management, including (1) precise determination of volume and number of trees to be removed in thinnings, (2) mathematical expression of changes in site quality due to drainage, and (3) regulation of the volume of cut.

LITERATURE CITED [2]

BAADER, G. 1939. Der Kiefernüberhaltbetrieb im hessischen Forstamt Eberstadt II. II Teil. Das Verhalten des Überhaltes. Allg. Forstu. Jagdztg. 115:141-148.

BISTRUP, C. 1951. Udjaevning af Stamtallet. (Smoothing the curve of tree number/ha.) Dansk Skovforen. Tidsskr. 36:521-530. (Summarized in Forestry Abstracts 14:83.)

BRAATHE, P. 1957. Thinnings in even-aged stands: A summary of European literature. Faculty of Forestry, University of New Brunswick, Fredericton.

BRIEGLEB, P. A. 1952. An approach to density measurement in Douglas fir. J. For. 50:529-536.

CHISMAN, H. H. and F. X. SCHUMACHER. 1940. On the tree-area ratio and certain of its applications. J. For. 38:311-317.

CZARNOWSKI, M. 1947a. Wstęp do hodowli Lasu. Pol. (Introduction to Silviculture.) Księgarnia Akademicka, Poznań. 145 pp.

CZARNOWSKI, M. 1947b. Kwadrat wysokości drzew jako wskaźnik ich normalnej więźby w drzewostanie. Pol. (Square of tree height as an index of normal spacing in the stand.) Roczn. Nauk. rol. 49:244-266. (Summarized in Biol. Abstr. 22; position 22214.)

---

2 Names of Russian authors between parentheses are spelled in the international bibliographical system of transliteration, which is used in libraries on the European continent.

DUERR, W. A. 1938. Comments on the general application of Gehrhardt's formula for approach toward normality. J. For. 36:600-604.

EYTINGEN, G. R. (ÈJTINGEN) 1946. Lesnaya opytnaya dacha 1865-1945. (Forest Experiment Station) 1865-1945. Moskva. p. 79.

EYTINGEN, G. R. (ÈJTINGEN) 1949. Vyzhivaemost' derev'ev v lesu. Rus. (Vitality of trees in forests.) Agrobiologiya, No. 1.

GEHRHARDT, E. 1930. Ertragstafeln für reine und gleichartige Hochwald-bestände von Eiche, Buche, Tanne, Fichte, Kiefer, Grüne Douglasie und Lärche. 2 Auflage. Springer, Berlin.

GEORGIEVSKI, N. P. (GEORGIEVSKIJ) 1948. O razvitii nasazhdeni pri rubkakh ukhoda. (On the development of thinned plantations.) Razvitie russkogo lesovodstva. Vol. I, Moskva-Leningrad, 1948, p. 172-173.

GEVORKIANTZ, S. R. 1937. The approach of northern hardwood stands to normality. J. For. 35:487-489.

HUMMEL, F. C. 1954. Definition of thinning treatments. Proceedings 11-ieme Congres. int. Union For. Res. Organ., Rome, 1953, p. 582-588. Firenze, 1954.

JEDLIŃSKI, W. et al. 1932. Badania właściwości struktury, rozwoju i przyrostu drzewostanów w Polsce. Pol. (Research of propriety of structure, development and growth in forest stands in Poland.) Warszawa, 1932.

KHIL'MI, G. F. (CHIL'MI) 1955. Biogeofizicheskaya teoriya i prognoz samoizrezhivaniya lesa. Rus. (Biogeophysical theory and prediction of reduction in number of trees per surface unit with increase in age.) Moskva, 1955.

KUNZE, M. 1918. Über den Einfluss der Anbaumethode auf der Ertrag der

gemeinen Kiefer. Mitt. aus der Königl. Sachs. forst. Versuchanstalt

zu Tharandt. Bd. I, H. 5. Paul Parey, Berlin.

ŁOMNICKI, A. 1935. Rachunek różniczkowy i całkowy dla potrzeb przyrod-

ników i techników. Pol. (Differential and integral calculus for

naturalists and engineers.) polsk. Akad. Um. Kraków, 1935.

LYNCH, D. W. 1958. Effects of stocking on site measurement and yield

of second-growth ponderosa pine in the Inland Empire. Intermoun-

tain For. Range. Exp. Sta. Research Paper 56.

McKINNEY, A.I., F. X. SCHUMACHER, and L. E. CHAIKEN. 1937. Construc-

tion of yield tables for normal loblolly pine stands. J. agric.

Res. 54:531-545.

MEYER, W. H. 1942. Yield of even-aged stands of loblolly pine in

northern Louisiana. Yale University, School of Forestry. Bull.

51.

PŁOŃSKI, W. 1937. Tablice zasobności i przyrostu drzewostanów. Sosna

(Yield and growth tables of forest stands. Scots pine.) Inst. Bad.

(Las. panst. Wars.) Warszawa, 1937.

REINECKE, L. H. 1933. Perfecting a stand-density index for even-aged

forests. J. agric. Res. 46:627-638.

SIMMONS, E. M. and G. L. SCHNUR. 1937. Effects of stand density on

mortality and growth of loblolly pine. J. agric. Res. 54:47-58.

SPURR, S. H. 1952. Forest Inventory. The Ronald Press Co., New York.

SUCHECKI, K. 1947. Równanie drzewostanu. (Equation of forest stand.)

Roczn. Nauk. rol. Poznań.

TYURIN, A. V. (TJURIN) 1928. Taksaciya lesa. (Forest Management.)

Moskva.

TKACHENKO, M. E. (TKAČENKO) 1939. Obshcheye lèsovodstvo. Rus. (General agriculture.) Leningrad.

U.S. FOREST SERVICE. 1929. Volume, yield, and stand tables for second-growth southern pines. U.S. Dep. Agric. Misc. Pub. 50.

VANSELOW, K. 1941. Einführung in die forstliche Zuwachs - und Ertragslehre. Sauerländer. Frankfurt a. M.

WALTHER, A. 1928. Einfuhrung in die mathematische Behandlung naturwissenschaftlicher Fragen. Springer, Berlin, p. 184.

WEBER, R. 1891. Lehrbuch der Forsteinrichtung. Springer, Berlin.

WEISE, W. 1880. Ertragstafeln für die Kiefer. Springer, Berlin.

WILSON, F. G. 1946. Numerical expression of stocking in terms of height. J. For. 44:758-761.

ZIMMERLE, H. 1938. Zuwachsuntersuchung bei der Fichte im fürstl. Forstbezirk Hartsfeldhausen. Allg. Forst - u. Jagdzt. 114:341-351.